THE AMATEUR KEEPER

To

TITCH ON YOUR 71st
                BIRTHDAY
                2008.

HOPE YOU FIND THIS BOOK
            USEFUL.

LOVE
        CHRIS & GORD
        XX.

Archie Coats

The Amateur Keeper

A HANDBOOK FOR THE SMALL SHOOT

INTRODUCTION BY COLIN WILLOCK

ILLUSTRATED BY WILLIAM GARFIT

Revised and updated with the help of The Game Conservancy Advisory Service, represented by Mike Swan.

ANDRE DEUTSCH

First published 1962 by Vista Books
Second edition published 1978 by André Deutsch Ltd.,
105–6 Great Russell St., London WC1B 3LJ
This revised edition published 1989 by André Deutsch Ltd.

British Library Cataloguing in Publication Data

Coats, Archie
   The amateur keeper. — 3rd ed.
   1. Game birds. Care & management. Great Britain.
   Amateurs' manuals
   I. Title
   636.6'3

ISBN 0 233 98456 9

Printed in Great Britain by
Ebenezer Baylis & Son Limited
The Trinity Press, Worcester, and London

TO MY WIFE

*Who nowadays has to do
all the work, and so is promoted
to Head Keeper.*

CONTENTS

LIST OF PLATES

Hopper photograph by Ian McCall
Other photographs and sketches by William Garfit

INTRODUCTION
by Colin Willock

I FIRST met Archie Coats in the early Fifties when I was writing for the magazines of Hulton Press. Jack Hargreaves, who later became famous as the producer and presenter of Southern Television's 'Out of Town' programme, was then my editor. Jack had heard of a remarkable man who made his living by shooting pigeons and sent me to interview him. The man, of course, remarkable indeed, turned out to be Archie Coats of Dummer in Hampshire. In a very short time I discovered that Archie Coats' expertise was not confined to outwitting and shooting wood pigeons. Here was a man deeply knowledgeable about the ways of birds and beasts, farming and forestry, the turn of the seasons and the vicissitudes of the climate, in fact he knew all about what would now be called the ecology of the English countryside. Since he was first and foremost a sportsman, all this naturally had a focal point. That focal point was shooting.

Among his other talents, Archie is a natural writer. He makes an awful fuss about writing and huffs and puffs a great deal about how difficult it is all going to be. But no one takes much notice of that, least of all his editor, me, or his publishers André Deutsch. Those who know Archie expect him to huff and puff a bit about most things, including running a shooting day or bawling out his friends who set up their pigeon hides or decoys in the wrong place. However, whether he is writing a book or marshalling a line of beaters, when it comes to the moment for action, all takes place with a fluency, enthusiasm and vast good-nature that shows in every page of this book.

1

Early in our friendship I convinced Archie that he must preserve and pass on his unique knowledge of foiling the evil deeds of the wily woodie. His first book *Pigeon Shooting* was the result and has deservedly become a country and sporting classic. I am not sure that I was wise to persuade Archie to make his store of pigeon knowledge generally available. *Pigeon Shooting* has helped to educate several generations of decoy experts who have become so proficient that, aided by the price paid for woodies to feed the Common Market, *Columba palumbus* appears to have become far more wary of decoy set-ups and even to have altered its habits considerably. But that is another story.

I next persuaded Archie to distil his unrivalled knowledge of running a small shoot. The result, first published in 1962, was *The Amateur Keeper*.

Even in 1962, the shooting picture was changing fast. There were still the big private shoots, of course, as well as big syndicates. But there was also a growing number of sportsmen with smaller, unkeepered acreages who longed to know how to make the best of their shoots on a do-it-yourself basis. Since *The Amateur Keeper* first appeared, D-I-Y in the shooting field has become more and more the thing. Nor are the costs the only things that have changed, as Archie points out. The time has obviously come to bring the book up to date – and here it is.

I first became convinced that Archie Coats was the ideal author for this book while being pressed into service to carry buckets of grit, ashes, corn and water round the ten acres that adjoin his home at Tower Hill Farm, Dummer. Such forced labour was often the prelude to a summer day's pigeon shooting with the Master. I always, out of keenness, arrived too early only to be told that in midsummer pigeons don't begin their second feed until at least midday. So I dutifully acted as occasional assistant keeper on Archie's Ten Acre shoot. During these tours of duty I learned much about how to keep pheasants at home and happy. Later, I was lucky to be asked to assist in garnering the fruits of Archie's labours. As he describes in this book, there are two shoots a season at Tower Hill. Each lasts for two hours and is followed by a stupendous lunch created by his wife, Prue Coats.*

I usually get invited to 'Tower Hill Two', which takes place just before Christmas. Last year we shot seventy-five pheasants! A few weeks previously, 'Tower Hill One' had produced around the same number of birds off ten acres! But then it was the year of that exceptional summer. This year, we shot half that number but it was still a remarkable result. As Archie points out, the same principles apply be the shoot large or small, and he has plenty of experience of running both kinds.

When out in the field with Coats, I have never failed to learn something. And I have derived enormous pleasure from the company of a personality so warm, generous and larger than life that if he didn't actually exist, Surtees would have to be re-incarnated to invent him! I am delighted that thousands of new readers will be able to share some of that knowledge and enthusiasm through these pages.

November 1988 What Archie wrote in 1962 and later in 1977 is still perfectly true – but, with the addition of The Game Conservancy's expertise, I think that this book will now be even more valuable to those who not only love their shooting, but want to participate as well.

COLIN WILLOCK

November 1988 Now promoted to Head Keeper Prue has taken a leaf out of Archie's book, and has written a superb cookery book – *Prue's Country Kitchen*. A cookery book with a difference, and illustrated as this one is by William Garfit, it is published by the World Pheasant Association, PO Box 5, Child Beale Wildlife Trust, Lower Basildon, Reading RG8 9PF.

FOREWORD

THIS book was first published in 1962 to help those who own or rent a small, even a tiny, shoot. Perhaps I can persuade those who believe that a small acreage is not worth bothering about to think again. For a little labour, which may soon turn to love, they will give their friends some fun, and be pleasantly surprised at what they can achieve. It is now 1988 and 'do-it-yourself' methods are more in vogue than ever. In bringing this book up to date, I find that nothing has basically changed in the running of a small shoot. The same rules apply – except that they cost more to put into action!

Of course certain things have altered, and they are dealt with as they occur in the various chapters, but my basic reasons for writing the book still stand.

If you treat birds right, they will stick around and will not let you down. That is the basis I work on. Keeping game means looking after birds and the same rules apply on the ten or the ten thousand acre shoot. There are three fundamental ways of treating birds right. Give them protection from their enemies, i.e. predators, provide them with cover or habitat to nest, live and sleep in, and with food all the year round. Alas, there may well be a fourth essential nowadays and that is protection from modern farming.

It pays every time to employ a professional keeper where the acreage permits. But few people can afford to pay a man to keeper less than five hundred acres unless it be 'part time' on the farm account, which is an excellent way of solving the problem. So I do not want my keeper friends to think that I am trying to do anyone out of a job by advising 'do-it-yourself' methods. I aim only to help those whose ground is too small to employ a full-time professional.

My friend William Garfit has taken the photographs and done all the drawings in this new edition. Some of the photographs used were taken on his own shoot, and I am most grateful to him for all his help. I am also grateful to Ian McCall of The Game Conservancy, for permission to use his photograph of hoppers.

November 1988 I am delighted, and indeed honoured, that The Game Conservancy, in the person of Mike Swan of their Advisory Service, has agreed to bring *The Amateur Keeper* up to date, as a joint effort. Apart from the prices in the 1977 edition being in pounds, shillings and pence, some new ideas have emerged. But once again I can say that nothing has basically changed in the running of any shoot, large or small. You will read, and see, that I carry an onion hoe and do this or that. Well, I used to but can't now because of being permanently on crutches, one of the reasons why my wife Prue has been promoted to Head Keeper. She now does all the work. I haven't changed the wording because that is indeed what *you* should do, you fit and lucky so-and-sos. So cherish the pleasure your small shoot will give you and share that pleasure with your friends.

1962
1977   The same rules apply—
1988

PREDATOR CONTROL

IF you do not make any attempt to control vermin on your shoot, then you do not deserve a shoot at all. My friends at The Game Conservancy prefer to call carnivorous birds and animals 'predators', but they would heartily agree with the rest of this statement. Personally, I consider the rat and the crow to be vermin first and last. The others have redeeming points. The stoat kills rats and the magpie eats pigeons' eggs, so perhaps they can fairly be classed as predators.

Some of the protected birds, like the buzzard, can also do harm on occasions. In the buzzard's case it is hardly his fault. When rabbits were plentiful, I doubt whether he ever looked at a bird except, maybe, a pigeon. But now he has to move further afield for his food, and we see far more buzzards in my part of Hampshire than before myxomatosis. Soon after the spread of myxie, stoats, too, seemed almost to die out, but with a few more rabbits around they are coming back. Nature quickly revolts when man tampers with the established order of things, but, given a chance, she very soon readjusts herself.

Part of the success of the running of a small shoot lies in having good relations with one's neighbours, and nothing is more annoying than to have a constant stream of vermin spreading onto your land from ground where no effort is made at control. And, mind you, vice versa!

I started this book by saying that if you treated birds right they would not let you down; if you don't control their enemies you let them down with a bang. The viewpoint expressed by some shooting men, 'Oh! there's always a few, we don't bother much,' sickens me, and shows the most lamentable lack of understanding. Such people really don't deserve to shoot anything at all, and certainly they will never have very much to shoot at, except possibly birds from over the boundary!

Vermin control obviously means setting traps, but the Law says that traps have to be looked at daily, which takes time. So it may be impossible with the smaller shoot to carry out a very ambitious programme. Which, then, are the vital months when at least some effort must be made? Obviously those between the early spring and the time birds go down to sit. So, in late February and March, weather permitting, start your trap line when the enemies of game are hungry and moving around. And carry on as late as you can. Do not forget the old maxim, 'The trap works while the keeper sleeps'; so very true since most of these creatures operate at night.

Dawn and dusk are the best times to take a walk with a gun and catch the unwary napping, but you will have better success and see more of what should and should not be on your ground by sitting still at various points of vantage and watching through binoculars. Perhaps this applies more to winged enemies who all have nesting plans and regular flight lines. So, if you see a magpie fly into a hawthorn bush at dusk, the chances are that you can go and blow her clean off the nest if you wait until it is almost dark.

The same thing applies to crows: they *have* to come back to the nest some time, particularly if there are young there, and you must just wait very quietly until one returns. This may well be practically in the dark, their normal hour for going to bed. They usually choose some rather conspicuous tree such as a Scot's pine, and the nest is fairly obvious; whereas the magpie's nest in thorn or ivy-covered tree is sometimes quite difficult to see. In both cases it is a mistake to blow up the nest. Wait until you can get the old bird, too. Then use the choke barrel from right underneath, and the other if she flies off – unless you are too blinded by the shower of twigs.

Rooks, too, must be kept under control and the young ones shot with a ·22 rifle as they come out of the nest, which you hope will happen before the leaf gets too thick. A very killing way to thin out the adult population of a too populated rookery is to flight them until it is quite dark. It is kinder to do this before the young are hatched, though it will mean that the survivors will have to lay again as the eggs will be chilled. However, there is a snag to this; by the time the second brood hatches, and 'comes out', the leaf will be so thick that you will not be able to see them.

Ralph Payne-Galwey said many years ago that no one can have many partridges if he has too many rooks. That is even more true today, as modern farming has left the cover far thinner. On the other hand it would be quite wrong to exterminate the rook, which is very fond of wireworms, leather-jackets and other farm pests. I personally believe that rooks are very intelligent creatures and if a few naughty ones are made examples of, the remainder quickly understand that eggs are not to be taken. While pigeon shooting, I shoot a good many 'rogue' rooks as well as many other winged enemies. If a lot come over, I leave them, but if a single one flies along, quartering the ground like any old black-backed gull, I have him quick.

Magpies and jays have their regular lines of flight along hedgerows and they perch on prominent trees. This behaviour coincides with the pigeon's habits. The cunning crow, funnily enough, is a sucker for dead pigeon decoys, and if you sit absolutely still in the hide, crows will often come right in. Jays are difficult to get hold of by yourself and more are shot at covert shoots than at any other time. If you drive a well-known line of flight to a friend concealed at the far end you can usually account for a few.

Most members of the crow family can be caught in cage traps of one sort or another. There are many different designs, some of which are more successful than others. Some of the best are described in The Game Conservancy's booklet No. 16 *Predator and Squirrel Control*.

With the advent of the Fenn trap, particularly the latest version, trapping has become relatively simple. Confident that your fingers will not suffer, though still with an eye on that nice safety catch, you can set it fine enough to catch a weasel. Ground vermin have set runs, or employ runs used by their intended victims. Very often these follow some feature – a rabbit fence, a bank, a furrow, or a footbridge over a stream. You have to learn a little basic woodcraft to be able to tell what a run looks like and if it is often used. No doubt there are some people who can tell exactly what species uses the run, but I don't aspire to such prowess except, maybe, to recognize the rat's which is greasy-looking. Apart from droppings, which you should be able to recognize, the main thing to look for is a track on which the earth is packed and which even looks a little wet or oily. This run will probably join up with another.

In Figure 1 you will see a small copse which adjoins a neighbour's wood, at the east end. There is a rabbit fence in between. There are two hedges on the south side and a strip and a rough bank which leads to your boundary on the north. These junctions, where ground vermin traffic must pass either when entering into, or departing from, your wood, are the places for your tunnel traps. To start with, they are the most likely places to make a catch, and by using them you are keeping the number of catching points to a minimum. In the sketch there are six positions marked O and six alternative positions marked Z. A full-time keeper would probably have traps at all twelve places, but you simply have not the time to look at all these. Therefore, trap all the O positions to start with and, if you are unsuccessful, move some of the traps to the Z positions. But only six traps are in use at one time, and the Z or O positions which are left vacant are not blocked, so that they serve as runs. If you find them being used again, you should have another go.

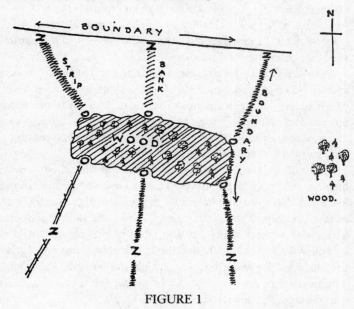

FIGURE 1

A trap should be kept in position for at least two to three weeks, and it takes two or three days for your smell to leave it when first set. New traps are best weathered before use – they should be bought in autumn and hung outdoors over winter before the spring trapping season. However, weasels and stoats have been caught in new traps within hours of being first set, so do not delay your campaign just to weather the traps.

There are many different ways of making a tunnel trap. The main points, apart from the siting, are that it must be just high enough to allow the trap to spring, just wide enough to ensure that whatever enters the tunnel must pass over the plate, and nice and dark inside. All the wicked are curious and will investigate a dark and, after a time, probably deliciously smelly hole. There are many materials (large drainpipes, old boards, corrugated iron, etc.) which can be used. Nature can often provide the best place; for instance, the run may pass through an old tree stump or root. Another safe bet is a footbridge or an old log over a stream. With some sods and branches and a little spade-work, most natural sites can be converted into the ideal spot for your trap.*

However, where I can't use a natural site I use four bricks and an old board approximately 30 inches long by 8 inches wide, which makes a nice permanent structure. This takes me about ten minutes to erect. Tools required are a spade, an onion hoe and a hedge knife with which to remove any surplus brambles, etc., so that one can see into the trap.

First cut six good sods with the spade and lay them handy, together with a good peg for the chain. Then scrape the ground level and dig a shallow half-inch depression, right on the run, to take the trap. Then set the Fenn, adjust the safety catch and fit for size so that it sits flat and snug in the depression. Try it both ways to see which way the run is best 'covered'. Leave the chain in the space between which you will put the bricks. The next step is to place the bricks in two pairs, two a side. As the photograph shows,† these should be placed round the trap in such a way that their ends face inwards, leaving just enough space for the run to enter and leave the tunnel. There will be a gap between each lot of bricks on both sides. You have to fiddle about with the exact position of the bricks until they are level, so

*See Game Conservancy Booklet, No. 16, *Predator and Squirrel Control*.
† See photograph.

that they will take the board which forms the roof of the trap. Lay the board on top of the bricks and adjust so that it projects some way above the run at both ends. Make certain that there is enough height for the trap to spring, though the depression should ensure this.

When everything fits, remove the board, take the trap out and set it as finely as you can; put it back again and fix the chain firmly into the ground, with the peg in the space between the bricks. I personally like to sprinkle a little dry earth on the plate before removing the safety catch; others practically bury the trap. Then put the board back carefully, fill in the gaps between the bricks and cover the whole roof with sods and grass, allowing some to dangle as a sort of curtain over the two entrances. Make certain it is dark inside and fill in any cracks. Lastly, use the onion hoe to scrape out the two entrances, so that the hole looks as if it has been newly worked, and thus more interesting to the evil-minded.

I have stressed that you must be careful. When you hear a loud snap just as you are putting the last sod on, you will know why! As a final touch, to keep Mrs Pheasant out you can stick one or two twigs in the ground outside the entrances.

Provided the trap is on the run, it should not be necessary to have a V-shaped 'lead in' of wire netting or brambles, but there may be places where you can make some sort of a barricade to steer the victim to his doom.

All this may seem a lot of work, but once it is done, you have a permanent trap which will last a long time. True every time you catch something, you have to take the sods and the board off and re-set. Nevertheless, this trap has advantages over others that are set right in the mouth of the tunnel, not the least of which is the safety angle.

Do not hang the victims up near the trap. They may act as a bait for other vermin but they will also act as an advert to the site of your traps and attract human interference. The keeper's gibbet can cause great offence to ordinary walkers and other countryside users and is best avoided.

Do not expect to catch vast numbers of evil-doers, but if a trap has not caught for some time, particularly in wet weather, it may be wise to re-set it and use your onion hoe to scrape out the tunnel. You can bet on it that stoats and weasels, if there are any around, will investigate your tunnel and if the trap is properly set, in due course they will make a mistake. The good keeper has confidence in his traps and takes it as a hopeful sign if they don't catch. But they must be serviced.

The grey squirrel is also an egg-stealer and as such should be dealt with, quite apart from his unsavoury forestry or market garden reputation. But where he can become the greatest bore is on your pheasant feeds, where he eats a lot of grain. You can tell he is there by little round holes bored in the litter; ditto the rat. There are two ways to catch them on the feed. One means of feeding pheasants, when labour and daily visits are impossible, is with bales of straw placed in a cone and with tailings poured in. The last bale acts as a roof. The corn is meant to dribble out at the sides; the pheasants scratch and more falls out. This is all very well but the bales also provide a lovely warm dry restaurant for grey squirrels and rats. Peg or tie one or more Fenn traps inside the bales and simply lay them on top of the tailings near the entrances. Scrimmaging around in the dark, your unwelcome guests soon make a mistake.

The other method is to use two drainpipes, large enough for a squirrel or rat to creep through. They are placed end to end, leaving enough space for the Fenn in between. You make a half-inch depression and fit the Fenn in snugly. Peg it down, and fix a wire shield cut from old rabbit netting in an arc over the trap, making sure that there is enough headroom for the trap to spring. A piece 18 inches by 8 inches is about right and this, too, must be well pegged down. Bait with a little corn inside the netting and use Warfarin in one of the drain pipes. Cover the netting with a few twigs and leaves. The corn is the trouble. If you don't use the wire netting, you will certainly catch a pheasant who will peck about until it springs the trap; it will be a very dead pheasant. And a barricade of sticks over the trap is not sufficient; any self-respecting old cock will knock it aside.

You can also account for squirrels at the end of March by blowing them out of their dreys. Use No 4 shot, stand directly underneath and give them the choke barrel. At this time there may well be young and you can tell the breeding dreys by their freshly-made look, often with oak leaves still attached to the branch. These are often sited in a crotch or in thicker cover such as an ivy-covered tree. But old man squirrel may be barred from the nursery and be sitting in one of the summer dreys which are usually rather lightly built. It is worth wasting a few cartridges to get him. Poles are not necessary.

I have always felt strongly that rats should be treated primarily as a farm responsibility and that their destruction should be paid for on the farm account. But on the small shoot, though the two sides (keepering and farming) must work in together, you simply cannot afford, as a shooting tenant, to allow *any* rats to remain on the shoot or on the boundaries thereof. It should be possible to divide the responsibility. Thus the farm looks after the barns, hedgerows, ricks, etc., adjacent to the crops, to which rats can do so much harm; and the shoot looks after the woods, especially the pheasant feeds, to which many rats are attracted as soon as the stubbles are ploughed. Whether the work is performed by contract or by the farm employees is no matter, but the rat is the partridge's enemy Number One and it is vital that the hedgerows be thoroughly 'done' with Warfarin, preferably three times a year and certainly twice. And by 'done' I mean enough visits have been made to ensure that on the last one, the holes or baiting points still have uneaten Warfarin in them.

The most telling times of year to apply Warfarin are just after the harvest, after Christmas or whenever the autumn ploughing is finished, and most important of all, in March before any birds have gone down. Observation should tell you where the survivors have got to and they must be dealt with whenever found. I cannot stress this enough; I have a nasty feeling, and so have many keepers, that the rat population may be on the up-grade.

Warfarin in its various forms was hailed as a final solution to the rat. So was 'myxie' to the bunny! But I think (and secretly hope in some ways) that the bunny is beating 'myxie', and I wonder if the rat is not getting used to Warfarin or breeding its effect out in some way.

Since writing this, there has been correspondence in the papers about rats becoming immune to Warfarin. Even where Warfarin resistance is known, there are other anti-coagulant poisons of a similar type which are effective. However, most of these are slightly more toxic to other forms of wildlife which might eat a dead rat. Warfarin still works well in most areas and should be chosen first unless you know that there are resistant rats in your area. Most reports of resistance are still due to inefficient baiting allowing some survivors. In which case the addition of a little sugar will make the bait more palatable.

Every pheasant feed, as soon as it is put down, should have one long drainpipe regularly filled, and kept filled, with Warfarin. This can be bought made up, but is expensive. It is far cheaper to mix your own brew, using any hen or pig mash as a basis which I personally get from the farm as and when I want it. But it is important to make the mixture carefully as per the instructions, and thereafter keep it dry. This is the main drawback to Warfarin; in wet weather it is useless to put it down a hole in a hedge as it quickly deteriorates. And though for a time it may help to fill in the hole, Warfarin needs to be watched. As long as it goes, you have to keep on supplying it.

Baiting points are best, and I like using a longish drainpipe which is watertight. It should be laid flat so that the rain can't run in and the Warfarin put well in the middle with a spoon spliced onto a stick. This keeps it drier and also prevents pheasants or other birds from eating it if it leaks out of the pipe. Though Warfarin does not often affect birds, it is best kept out of the way of livestock or dogs.

The drainpipe should be placed on the sheltered side of one of the bales used at the feed for birds to sit on. Rats tend to burrow in or 'run' these bales, so they soon find the stuff. It is worth looking near a feed, as rats often make their holes quite close and the runs will lead you to them. In dry weather you can dose the runs as well. I am a firm believer in the theory that you should fill the drainpipe with as much Warfarin as it will hold without its getting wet. Others say that it should be put down in small quantities and often. This takes time and I prefer to give hungry rats a bellyful of Warfarin rather than my precious pheasant food.

To conserve Warfarin, and keep it dry, I now dig out a sort of nest under the 'sitting' bale on the feeds, line it with a bit of polythene and/or dry straw and put the Warfarin mix on top. Dig out a run as you would for a tunnel trap. When feeding, lift the bale to see if you have had any customers, but have a stick handy, as it is surprising how often you find a rat at home. They themselves use bales to build a nest under so you are doing a natural, and therefore sensible thing. I now think that this is a better bet than the drainpipe system.

Cymag is also effective, a little being spooned well down each hole of a colony, and the holes filled up. The moisture in the atmosphere causes a gas to form and it then seeps throughout the burrow. If any of the holes are opened after a 24-hour interval, you know there have been some escapes. You should never work alone with Cymag; do not inhale the gas or let the powder get on your clothes, and in case of accidents always carry the antidote with you. Buy it when you buy the Cymag.

Boundary hedges are often a problem, but it is surely not too much to suggest that the two owners get together and make some arrangement, as both sides must be dealt with at the same time. And whatever method you use, get rid of the rats and keep on at the job. If you get rid of the last one you will be the first to do so!

For some people, fox-hunting is the only sport, while for others shooting takes pride of place. A lucky few manage to do both. On the other side of the fence there sit (and sometimes shout) a very large body of people who neither hunt nor shoot and would dearly love to see both sports abolished. These people are well organized and provide a definite and increasing threat to all sport. So shooting and fox-hunting men should try to live together peacefully and join forces in order to present a united front to the 'Anti's'. The British Field Sports Society exists partly for this reason and should be supported by everyone who has the interest of his sport at heart. A lot of us are also members of the RSPCA, but few take the trouble to vote at the meetings – where a minority vote might one day result in an act of Parliament which might make us all look very silly indeed.

Having written these prophetic words in 1962, it is interesting to see the sorry mess this otherwise excellent Society's Council has got itself into in regard to sport. I imagine financial mess as well, as a lot of their subscriptions come from those people whose legitimate sport they would like to stop.

This business of fox-hunter and game-shooter holding hands is, of course, all very well in theory, but it is often difficult in practice. What does the shooting man do (let alone say) when he finds a hen partridge taken off the nest, perhaps two days before she was due to hatch off, or his young poults, just put into covert, lying headless in the rides? And what does the Master say when a member reports on that earth in the old pit at Mr So-and-So's: 'Lovely litter of cubs there was; now it's filled in and silent, and you can't go near the place without a gas mask for the stink of Cymag about.'

Well, there you are, what is the answer? I don't really know, but there are certain facts which should be accepted. First and foremost, as I have suggested, the survival of all field sports depends on a solid front being shown by all sportsmen. Secondly, a hunt only wants to find one fox when it draws your coverts, but it *does* expect to find that fox. No shoot, and in particular no partridge shoot, can ever be much good if there are too many foxes. But large pheasant shoots dependent on many reared birds often suffer very little from a few foxes, there being enough for all.

How should the small shoot deal with this vexed question? Local conditions must play an enormous part and the only way

I can give any guide is by suggesting very tentatively what I do myself. My ten acres at Tower Hill (my ewe lamb) I keep clear of foxes all the year round, by every means. I consider this quite reasonable as ten acres is far too small an area in which to allow Reynard to make a permanent home. Also the hunt never draw it, and I have never known them run anywhere near it.

On the larger shoot that I keeper, which is visited (though seldom) by the hunt, I destroy if I can any fox which is being 'naughty' – i.e. taking birds off the nest. There are two earths. Based on neighbouring keepers' reports, we agree to gas or destroy all litters or potential litters, save one. Fox-driving in March may account for outliers. The main thing is to reduce your fox population in an area to a minimum before, and keep it that way during, the nesting season. When I say 'destroy litters', I include the vixen. If you destroy her cubs and she lives, she will quite understandably go on the rampage and take every bird she can find off the nest. It is surprising how many people are ignorant of this fact. So if you are going to do the job, do it properly; if you get her first, you can obviously get the litter afterwards.

Nature sees to it that birds, when they are sufficiently grown, can take care of themselves, and I do not think that foxes do much damage after the middle of September, unless it be with poults put very late to covert. Therefore, when cub-hunting starts you should be happy to tell the Master, when he rings up and says he would like to come next week, that there are some cubs around.

Thus it is the amateur or full-time keeper's job to see that everybody is happy. If he has to destroy foxes, let him do it quietly and without fuss or publicity. No employer should ever have to say, either, 'Gaiters, there are too many foxes,' or 'Why wasn't there a fox when they met last Saturday?' And no owner, tenant, or any of their guns should ever shoot a fox at a pheasant stand, unless specifically asked to do so by the host. This is the quickest way to create bad blood between hunt and shoot that I know of. In return, a keeper will expect to know the dates of adjacent meets as well as those on his own ground.

Then he can stop the earth in good time. And, in return for this service, he will not expect hounds to draw his coverts just before his 'big days'; and he *will* expect hounds to be stopped if by chance they run onto his ground just before such a shoot. One realizes that the latter is not always possible, but at least an effort could be made.

I should like to suggest, too, that hounds drawing a covert in fact do very little harm to grown wild birds and a hell of a lot of good to reared ones. They may in this way be taught to fly and so see what the world looks like outside the parent covert. They used to be encouraged to do this, and it is a pity it has gone out of fashion.

Anyway, foxes are a difficult subject and perhaps one's conscience is the best guide to go by!

The 'dustbin fox' who lives partly on garbage on new housing estates and dines out as a treat on your pheasants, if you happen to shoot the adjacent agricultural land, is a relatively new problem on the shooting scene.

I recently asked a renowned Master of Foxhounds what his views on these 'critturs' were. Apart from being unprintable they can be summed up as follows: 'The dustbin fox is no use to the hunt, because it never goes away, but runs in a circle back to its inhabited area, using the vicinity of roads, railways and motorways to do so. As all these are potential hazards to running hounds, there is no future in it.'

On being asked what he would do if he had a shoot (as I have) close to housing estates, he replied 'shoot or snare them'. So there you are and therefore the fox drive and the wire are your two best bets. Both have technical problems, and it is far better to get help from a professional keeper on both points. Wires are perfectly legal, but like traps, have to be visited daily. I can 'read' a fox track well enough, but I am not clever at setting these devices. All experts have their own ways of doing it, and you are now limited to the free-running snare, so I do not intend to stick my neck out on this one. Do as I say – get advice – then you can't blame me!

Now for cats. Anyone who has any knowledge at all of their charming habits will agree without any argument that there are only two sorts of cat: dear, good, well-fed pussies who don't go further than the garden or your neighbour's back door, and nasty, cruel, half-starved creatures who are about the worst predators you can think of. There is only one thing to do about the latter – get them, by fair means or foul, and get them quickly and bury them. It is a sad comment on our society, but it is a fact that some people going on holiday simply let their pussy out of the car door on the way. One cannot therefore blame these cats, but they do a shoot no good; I fear the same applies to dogs.

It is difficult to mention dogs under the heading of vermin or predator control, but the marauding dog can be as great a menace as anything. There is only one way to go about this problem; find out the owner and try to get him to restrain his dog, as he must by law. If this does not work, you must go to the local police officer and get him to lodge a formal complaint. You must be quite firm about this, since once a dog has got into the hunting habit it is very difficult to cure.

Alas, a new and very nasty predator has come on the scene. The mink. Killers for fun, they are a real menace to any bird, not only game birds. Fond of water, your duck population will suffer, as will any trout in a pond. They are, thank goodness, easy to trap. Can you recognize their footmark? See page 22.

Control or destruction of the enemies of game should not become too much of a chore or bore, otherwise the pleasure of your small shoot is marred. The great thing is to undertake something. If you have done your best and can see the results of it, you get a nice smug feeling of 'well, I have done my bit. It's up to the pheasants to get on with it.' And they will, too, if you give them half a chance.

A good trapper is a good naturalist who uses what his eyes and his sense of smell tell him. He gradually learns what a 'run' looks like, how often it is used and, maybe eventually, by whom. Then he starts to learn where to look for the culprit. It is astonishing how few people recognize the droppings of the birds and creatures who inhabit their woods. There are so many things to look at and recognize, and each tells its story – and very fascinating this is, too. Look at the tracks in the snow: in dry weather look for footprints where bird and beast go to drink at a puddle still left in the tractor rut. You didn't think there was a stoat around, did you? But there is the proof in writing in the mud.* Can you tell that little mound of leaves for what it is? It is the winter home of Mrs Hedgehog.

To me the ability to read the country scene is one of the greatest joys and satisfactions of running a small shoot.

*A most excellent book is *Tracks and Signs of British Animals*, by Alfred Leutscher, published by the Cleaver Hume Press.

Making birds work for their food helps to keep them at home. Strategically sited heaps of cow or horse dung against a sheltered tree are valuable. On the feed itself, the litter should be kicked around, or up against a bank or tree. The birds also appreciate the provision of a 'sitty' bale.

On the feed or in the release area much can be done to provide 'home comforts'. Drinkers are essential; extra cover can be provided with brushwood and branches and grit must be available. Baiting points for rats underneath bales are effective and safe.

Roosting cover is essential for the small shoot. Artificial stubble can be provided on plogh or fallow land.

Three alternative methods of rearing for the small shoot: a brooder in this case with young duck, in a garage or shed; broodies – women's work; and some 'tired ladies' being released – slowly does it.

FEEDING AND TACTICS

PHEASANTS and partridges like to eat just as you and I do, well and regularly the whole year round. In all shoots there comes a time when there is little more you can do to protect your birds or give them better living quarters. To hang on to them when their natural food is getting short, you must start feeding, and this is surely one of the best ways of treating them right. A lot of people attach great importance to feeding at regular hours. On the small shoot this may be well-nigh impossible, and I have found out that so long as they get food from time to time they will stick around. There is only one time not to feed, and that is when they are going up to roost. However, birds do like to go to bed on a full crop so feeding in the afternoon in preferred roosting areas can be a good idea. It helps to draw birds home to a safe roost. You might also think of feeding a small strip of kale or game crop at night to avoid disturbance during the day.

Pheasants take their young into the corn as soon as they can get about, which means as soon as they are dry after hatching. They seem to prefer wheat to barley, perhaps because it is less dense; and on downland there is often little choice, barley being predominant. Young pheasants can eat some seeds as well as insects almost as soon as they are born, and so their chances of survival are higher than those of the partridge whose chicks must have insects for the first two or three weeks of their lives. On the other hand both cock and hen partridges are very much on the job as parents, whereas the hen pheasant looks after her brood alone and sometimes rather carelessly at that. There is little you can do to help the partridges in the summer months, unless it is very dry, and on the small shoot, apart from siting pheasant feeds so that partridges can get at them, your problems do not arise until the time for winter feeding draws nigh.

Perhaps permanent dusting places or shelters are something you *can* do to make life easier for the partridges, and indeed for pheasants too. How to make them is explained in 'Improving your Prospects' (see Photographs). Otherwise I carry a hoe on my rounds and scratch out places in suitable sunny and sheltered areas. The ash from any hedge clipping or wood fires is preferred, but any old straw can be burnt and they will use the remains to dust in.

The summer of 1976 made a nonsense of all normal routine. The dew virtually failed and I had to do something, and do it quickly, to provide water in places where it was not available. Of course the pheasants had water containers at each feed but the pundits will tell you that partridges don't need watering. Well, that may be so in normal years, but it was not so then and I saw them using my polythene sack drinking places. I am quite proud of these and they are a cheap and satisfactory way of salving your conscience in times of stress. You find a shady and sheltered place, preferably by or in a hedge or covert which you know by observation is frequented by birds. It might well tie in with a winter feed area. You dig a shallow depression, with sloping sides, and line it with two polythene sacks which have not got holes in them. You then heap earth and stones around the edges, or better still, cut sods and put them around the perimeters. The whole idea is to make them look as natural as possible. I prefer black polythene but I don't think it really matters. Fill these with water and top up when required. I usually put a few large stones in the bottom and a few branches across in case chicks fall in.

Occasionally a miracle happens and you realize that you have somehow made an artificial dew pond. I have one which has not been repaired for seven years. Perhaps mud has cemented everything together. I wish I knew how this came about.

There is not much need to feed pheasants from May until harvest, though on softwood forestry land where there is no cereal, it may pay to keep a feed or two going. With the corn thus provided they can probably get enough local food from grass seeds, anthills, etc. Anything fenced in with wire netting, such as forestry or newly-planted strips, is inclined to be a death trap for young pheasants whose mum may quite easily fly over into the corn and leave them behind. I feed my own Christmas trees all year round, having no cereals, and certainly manage to hold a brood or two which never seem to leave them (though perhaps this last is wishful thinking on my part). On a tiny acreage, provided there is holding cover, the idea is that the hens will nest near their local restaurant. As it provides their drink as well, you hope they will bring their broods to this certain source of food.

On any shoot, I am quite certain that as soon as you know a field is to be combined in two or three days' time, you should make a feed in any adjacent coppice, hedge or wood where you hope to hold birds; or if there is kale or roots adjoining, you should start to feed them. Thus, however much they may still have to eat on the stubble, they will have an alternative and, we hope, sheltered place to fall back on in bad weather or when the field is disturbed. In this way you are most likely to hold the birds which have been born locally. The smaller the shoot, the more important this method becomes. People say that pheasants stray. So they may do, later. But if you get hold of them when young and give them a nice regular dining place, they will come back for more like good customers. Anyway, I don't think that *wild* birds want to stray if the food is there. They are parochially minded and know where home is.

This particularly applies to wild partridges. The small shoot should never worry about driving partridges off the ground, they will be back again on their territory.

I now feel that there is another good reason for making your feeds before harvest. I have observed that wild birds seem to play host to released ones. You would think that they would hardly welcome intruders on their feeds – yet they seem to do so. Of course you get the odd jealous cock, but he is just as liable to clobber young chicks (perhaps his own blood), nasty old man!

With modern farming methods, it is usually all too soon that the field is ploughed; sooner or later you will have to feed and it had better be sooner before someone else beats you to it. So you might as well site your feeds to fit in with your shooting plans.

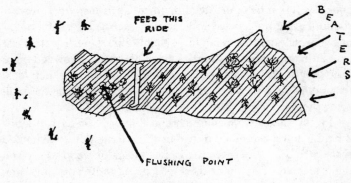

FIGURE 2

By the end of harvest you should have most of your tactical feeds working and can tell by the droppings and the way they are scratched up, whether they have 'taken'. If they have, the chances are that, disasters apart, you will hold the birds until you shoot. Though I will explain later how to obtain and store your grain from the drier, the place you choose to feed it is perhaps more important than the method employed. But one thing is certain: be very careful how and where you throw tailings about. If any fall on ground sown for seed, you will be most unpopular with the farmer. Obviously, this applies particularly to feeds in hedgerows.

Normally speaking, your feed should be sited between where your beaters start and the flushing point beyond which your guns stand. Figure 2 shows a straightforward stand. Here your beaters get behind the birds; they may even blank-in some open country outside into the wood. But we hope that most of the birds are on the feed already and are thus driven into the flushing point where they take off over the guns. Behind the guns should be some field or wood which the birds know and to which they are quite willing to fly.

Figure 3 shows the feed sited in hedge A which slopes uphill to a small coppice, where there is another feed. Thus both groups of birds probably know where the two feeds are. The drill here is to stop the coppice, then blank hedge A uphill to the coppice; hedge A is then stopped at the junction. The beaters go round to join the original stops and all drive the coppice back over the guns, who have taken their places after the blanking-in operation. Pheasants are quite happy to fly back to their feed area.

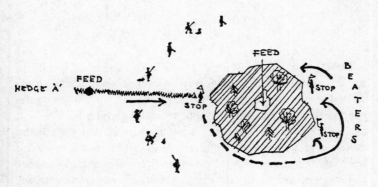

FIGURE 3

Figure 4 shows two long hedgerows or belts which join at
an angle. There might be a pit where they join, or you might be
able to have something planted specially. Feed the junction and
have one lot of beaters drive in each hedgerow or strip towards
it. Put two walking guns on each and let the remainder surround
the junction. The walking guns should stand back when they get
near the standing guns.

I am very keen on driving pheasants towards each other
as they often fly unexpectedly well, particularly in flat country.
The method is successful with strips of kale, mustard, etc., and
is really based on the old Continental way of driving partridges,
when a large area of country was surrounded in a circle, there
being about forty guns and probably 150 beaters.

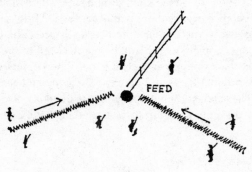

FIGURE 4

I once took part in such a shoot. At the sound of the horn,
the enormous circle (I expect we covered over 1,000 acres)
started slowly advancing, guns being spaced evenly amongst the
beaters. We were meant to shoot everything going back – both
hares and partridges. But what happened was that we got the
most marvellous driven shots from birds put up by the opposing
line, and it was perfectly safe to take these at any angle as they
were well up. When the circle was about half a mile in diameter,
the guns stood back at another horn signal and the beaters went
very slowly on. By this time there was an incredible amount of

stuff in the 'net' and I must admit that there was quite a lot of lead flying around – some of it where it shouldn't have been! But the partridges and the few pheasants that there were flew really magnificently, and it was very flat land indeed. The German word for this tactic is *Die Umkreise*. Figs 3 and 4 are what are known as 'Coats Manoeuvres' and there is always a groan when I make the other two members of my little syndicate carry them out. I have to explain very patiently! Almost all my feeds in any given area are based on the *Hin und Her* system which requires two feeds and allows you to drive the birds towards each other, with the result that they spread out and fly much better.

A change of direction in the beat may often fool birds and cause them to fly faster, particularly old cocks at the end of the season. Figure 5 shows a field of kale which has been drilled north–south for three-quarters of its length and, by request, east–west for the remainder. At the eastern end there is a nice fall in the ground and the next stand is a plantation about half a mile away. Blank the field down the drills from north to south; it is even better if you can have a strip cut (and feed it) where the two drills meet. The birds will run across the feed strip into the southern quarter. Then take the beaters round to the west end, leaving some as stops along the feed strip, and drive the southern quarter along the drills towards the east where the guns are standing in the hollow. Beater-guns should walk on both sides on the first part of the manoeuvre, and one of them walk along the feed ride and stand back in the second part. Birds are quite happy to fly to the plantation, which is already stopped and which will be a return drive. If the wind is different and you think the cocks know all about this game, do it in reverse.

Figure 6 shows a strip of kale adjoining a wood. The obvious method would be to drive the kale towards the wood, but you know by bitter experience that the birds will flop out at the end and won't be worth shooting. Luckily there is nothing very enticing for the birds to fly to at the north end of the kale. So do the brave thing, especially if there is a decent wind from the north-west. Relying on your birds to come back home, first put three beaters with flags around the north end of the kale. Then drive the kale from the wood towards them and bring in your guns to stand across the kale, perhaps in a semicircle, as far back as the length of the strip allows. As the beaters get on, birds should fly back of their own accord, helped by a wave from the flag men and the wind. This can be good fun and is one of the best ways of showing reared birds, if they can be enticed to leave their home wood. Feed the edges, about three-quarters of the way up the kale.

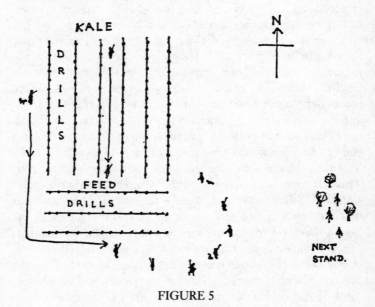

FIGURE 5

Whenever you want to have a stand, site your feed so that it fits in with your general plan, but if possible have an alternative up your sleeve. At least you will be able to start with the fond hope that your birds are in the right place at the right time, though this does not work out in practice as often as it might. We all know that sad lament, 'Well, there were twenty of the so-and-so's on that feed yesterday.'

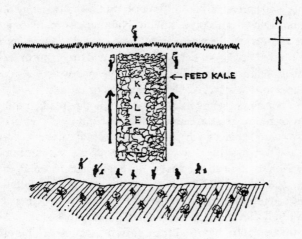

FIGURE 6

For the small shoot where time and labour are all-important, the quickest method of feeding may be the best. But there is no doubt in my mind that the old-fashioned straw feed gives the best results. With hopper-feeding, birds can peck all they require in a short time and they then wander off to see what goes on elsewhere. In the straw feed or shallow litter, they have to scratch for it and so take longer; and I think they enjoy it too, just as the old farmyard hen obviously likes kicking things around.

I prefer several small feeds, particularly if I can site them so that both pheasants and partridges share. Otherwise the obvious single place to choose is a ride which is easily reached, possibly by Landrover, and is probably sheltered; it is better still if it is sunny as well. Many keepers prefer the feed ride to stretch from one end of a wood to the other but in the direction of the beat – i.e. the way in which the wood will be driven. However, these take time to feed and are hardly practical for the small shoot.

When I can get them, I prefer barley straw bales. Barley straw seems to get less mucky and sodden than wheat straw, and the bales last longer in the open. I like to use four bales to a feed. The first is opened and spread, either in a line about thirty yards long down a ride, or in a circle in a pit or hollow. Number 2 is spare for adding to the straw when the weather has done its worst. Numbers 3 and 4 are for the birds to sit on; pheasants love to preen on straw bales and may well use them as look-outs. The last two are also useful to house your Warfarin-filled drainpipes or rat nests.

I do not use so many bales on a small hedge feed, and indeed leaves or rough grass are an excellent substitute as they are both highly 'scratchable' and dry out quickly. I often carry a fork when I feed, and turn over the straw so that the grain is lightly buried. This foils to some extent all the smaller birds and pigeons which eat a lot of the feed. Nowadays if your feeds are near human habitation or farms, as mine are, it is the collared doves which are a menace. At Tower Hill I reckon I have had to put down a bucket of feed extra daily to keep both them and the pheasants supplied. This applies particularly to the afternoon or artificial stubble feeds, which, by the time the pheasants got there had little left. So this is another good reason for kicking the litter around and covering the food up, but I am glad to hear that these pests are no longer protected. Turning it over helps to keep it dry. This, and adding fresh straw, helps to prevent any 'fungus' diseases. Heaven knows what we will do (pigeon shooters included) if farmers go over exclusively to those horrid, large round bales!

When you first make your feed, go canny with the straw. If your litter is too deep, birds won't be able to turn it over. If the feed is properly worked, they should really keep it in the correct state themselves. When you see it getting a bit bare, add fresh straw. I always do this, for some reason, for the last two feeds before the shoot, whether I am using a 'Keep-at-home' brew or not. Perhaps the fresh straw adds interest and, anyway, guests who see the feed will at least give you credit for taking some trouble!

Your feeds are the barometer of your shoot. If they are worked you need not worry. If they are not worked you may take it that something has happened. This is why I prefer shallow litter feeds to all other methods, because you can learn so much from them.

Today I realize how true it was to say that the feeds are the barometer of your shoot. Perhaps I should now add that the droppings under your roosting tree areas are another indication of what you have on the ground.

I always approach my feeds quietly, though with reared birds many keepers advocate making the same noise – a whistle perhaps – so that the birds recognize the 'scoff's up' signal. Anyway, I like to see what runs off, even if it is only a grey squirrel. But do not be discouraged if you do not see much. Some days you see a lot and others you see nothing, though, of course, your best chance is in the very early morning. The important thing is that the food should be gone and the straw well and truly scratched up. If there are no little pock marks in the litter, there are no squirrels. And if there is some Warfarin left in the drainpipe or under the bales, your rat problem is in hand.

On the first day of snow, I get frightfully excited and dash madly out to feed in the quite unnecessary fear that my charges will starve. Do not be worried if you see little movement or tracks in the snow – everything seems paralysed at first and you think that the worst has happened. But take a fork with you; they will thank you for opening up the feeds. Soon the tell-tale marks will tell you to whom you are playing host. Do not grudge small birds (there is always one robin who frequents every feed) a little of the pheasant food. If the snow lasts, a little exercise in tracking may lead you to where those rats are living.

The hopper is an excellent labour-saving device, particularly for winter-feeding, but if it can be used in conjunction with the scratch feed, so much the better. Hoppers can be made on the 'do-it-yourself' system and I can do no better than to refer you to Game Conservancy Booklet 14, *Game in Winter*. But we still prefer to feed by hand at Tower Hill. Hoppers can allow birds to fill up quickly and go for a walk. Scratching around takes time. But for winter feeding, when you want to keep your birds alive and kicking, rather than around the flushing points, hoppers pay off. (See photo.)

I think it is better to site a hopper, or any other feed for that matter, where you have seen birds rather than site it just anywhere and hope they will find it. But the same principles of shelter apply.

It is often useful to have some old drums or broken down freezers placed at strategic points on your shoot, if possible next to a track which is negotiable by Landrover or tractor. Use these as dry storage dumps for your feed. Thus you can replenish your feedbag and so save much carrying. The only vital thing is a good watertight lid and perhaps a padlock, particularly if anyone nearby keeps chickens!

Pyramids of straw bales can also be made and filled with tailings so that the corn trickles out of the side, where bales join. The top bale provides a roof. Once the pheasants find this pyramid they should scratch sufficiently for more to fall down; it is in fact a sort of hopper. The drawbacks are that pyramids provide a wonderful restaurant for rats and grey squirrels and the corn is inclined to grow mouldy even if the roof is completely waterproof. However, you will see from the previous chapter that they provide an excellent place to catch Messrs *Rattus norvegicus* and *Sciurus carolinensis*. There are various other gadgets which can be used for feeding, but if you stick to the old straw litter you won't go far wrong. One thing is certain; given the birds to start with, the success of your small shoot depends to a great extent on your feeding arrangements.

How often one feeds depends on the time available. Tower Hill is fed every day; on shoots I look after, and which entail a longish Landrover journey to visit, I try to feed twice and sometimes three times a week during the shooting season, and I like to step it up to once every two days a week before a shoot. And I simply *have* to feed the day before a shoot, though this is the day on which you never see anything and are usually in the depths of despair by the end of your round!

It is a mistake to feed too heavily; apart from the expense, your feed simply becomes a hopper and does not fulfil its purpose of keeping birds around. You might argue that if you fed heavily on a Monday, using as much feed as on a normal twice-a-week basis, this would see you through to the following Monday.

Unfortunately, it does not seem to work out that way, and when you go there on the Thursday everything has disappeared as quickly as if you had used the normal ration. In practice hand feeding works best when carried out on a daily basis. If you cannot manage this, a combination of plenty of hoppers to avoid trough competition, and straw to scratch in makes considerable sense. The Game Conservancy's booklet No 14 *Game in Winter* goes into this in some detail.

It is sensible to feed as soon after your shoot as possible, to reassure the survivors and start to build up your stock for the next time over. You may be able to fit this in with picking-up. There is a tendency to say, 'Thank God that's over,' and relax for a bit, but like all such tendencies you should at least try to resist it.

Some keepers feed their birds too heavily in an effort to keep them together. As a result they fly badly, being loath to leave the feeds in their home covert. It is understandable that they are frightened of losing their birds and keep on driving them back home. But this results in the poor things having no idea what the outside world looks like. When asked to fly away from the only place they know, they simply refuse or go back. Those that do come out are hardly worth shooting.

The old way of driving coverts blank, that is just beating them and not shooting them, before shooting days was a good idea (though impracticable nowadays); it mixed the birds up and made them a bit wild. In its place, if I had a shoot where birds were reared, I would always try to blank them away from home and fly them back again, at least for the first time over. They may learn to do better as the season goes on. So beware: give your birds just enough to keep them interested and wondering 'when that so-and-so is coming round again', but do not turn them into barnyard fowls.

Most keepers still think, even at the current appalling price of £120 per tonne, that their reared birds must have only best quality wheat. I have never found this necessary; which is just as well, as small shoots on a shoestring budget simply cannot afford it. I do not see why keepers on large shoots should not use Nature's food, the good and the poor as it would be on any normal stubble field. At least their employers would be a little better off. But there exists an understandable feeling that maybe their neighbours are using a better quality feed which will cause their birds to walk! Be that as it may, a small shoot must use as much from the drier as possible, no matter how 'ropey'. Make piles on your garage floor. Add as much 'seconds' wheat as you can afford and try and glean any maize cobs. It is surprising how many are left on the ground when the crop is cut for silage. Mix up the whole lot very thoroughly, the best way is to turn the heap completely over with a shovel, and then reverse the process. Store in polythene bags or sacks to a weight which you can easily carry. Don't, as usually happens to me, clean out all the rats on your feeds and forget the ones in your barn or storage place. An old deep-freeze cabinet makes a first-class dry and rat-proof food store.

Pigeon shooters can add the contents of their 'bags' crops including acorns and beech mast in season. Send the children out to pick up acorns. Stamp on them or hit them with a maul, on a concrete floor. Thus kibbled, pheasants love them. If you can find some grass seed, preferably mixed with grain from the drier you will find that hen pheasants especially go for it in a big way.

Once again, whatever you do, particularly in winter feeding when the partridges will be glad of almost anything you can produce, be careful where you put it. Farmers, especially those who grow seed quality crops will otherwise not love you much, and your 'dryer' source may dry up!

The diehards think a keeper should use only his feet on which to do his rounds. They condemn the use of a Landrover to feed or go round the traps. This is sheer old-fashioned nonsense, and the small shoot's ever-present problems of time and labour are particularly helped by having the part-time use of one of these excellent vehicles. I say categorically that I could not do without a Landrover; nor could the farm manager who does the feeding when I can't. Almost all the feeds are accessible by Landrover and those that are not require only short circular walks. All the traps are sited on, or very near, all-the-year-round tracks. In most seasons there are fifteen pheasant, or dual partridge/pheasant, feeds and usually another eight partridge feeds to get round, in the winter a lot more. Carrying the corn in sacks weighing not more than 25lb, the whole thing can be covered in about three hours. And this includes filling up the feed bins, looking at the traps, putting down fresh straw, Warfarin, etc.

Game birds do not worry about tractors and the general farm movements to which they are quite accustomed; and you can often see far more from your Landrover than you can on your flat feet. In the late afternoon, when birds come out to feed, the combination of a Landrover and a pair of binoculars will show you better than anything else what you have on the ground. If you are keen to count your partridge pairs at the end of March, this is the way to do it. You often spot vermin from your point of vantage and it is a good idea to carry a gun with you. But make certain that you have a rack made for it, as Landrovers can do unkind things to guns left haphazardly in them. There are also excellent racks on the market for shooting days, which prevent small boys, and dogs like mine, which jump into the back of a Landrover without looking where their great feet are going, from doing their worst!

It is nice, too, to think of the not so young (let alone some of those flourishing farmers who have put on a bit of flesh) who would be hard-pressed to do a day's shooting without the aid of some conveyance to transport them from stand to stand. And there is now little excuse for the girls to say, 'we will come out, but only after lunch.' No woman can get away with that on this man's shoot. If they are going to eat Prue's gourmet lunch they have to sing for it, which means beating, or for the more elderly, stopping.

WINTER FEEDING

LET us hope that you have had a good season and that 'cocks only and no partridges' is the order of the day at your Christmas shoot. You will probably have finished shooting partridges before then, or to be more accurate the partridges will have seen to it that they escape, particularly on a small acreage. Though it can be very frustrating if you are running a late partridge day, I rather enjoy seeing the almost incredible way in which they seem to size up the situation at a glance and go sliding out on that unguarded flank.

There is a school of thought which maintains that 'It does not matter how many partridges you shoot. Nature will see to it that you only have as many pairs as the ground will stand'. This is perfectly true up to a point, and that point is only a question of food and more living-space – which you may be able to provide. But partridges are such charming birds and pair so early in the right weather that I prefer to give them the benefit of the doubt and let them be. Certainly your guns should be instructed on a late shoot to take coveys only and leave the pairs.

If you are entirely reliant on wild pheasants, you have simply got to leave a reasonable stock of hens. Most keepers say that you can't shoot enough cocks and this can be true, though I personally believe that hens come to cocks as much as the other way round; but perhaps that is a modern trend that they have learnt from us! I know that too many hen pheasants may result in partridge nests being 'over-laid', but the small shoot can't have it both ways! Given plenty of good habitat, there should be nesting space for all.

There now comes the point which I consider to be only second in importance to the control of the enemies of game. Your birds have provided you with good sport, and now it is your turn to help them when they most need it. And in so doing to help your shoot enormously. Modern farming ensures a pretty barren and hungry landscape for the real winter months. Too many people, having finished their shooting, forget the birds until the next season comes around. And then they gripe if there aren't many. If they are the sort who are content to stand behind a hedge or at the covertside, and have birds driven over them without knowing or caring about the whys or wherefores, counting only the size of the bag as their measure of success of a day's shooting, then this book is not for them.*

Luckily, more and more people are becoming aware of the reasons and the necessity for winter feeding, even if only because they have seen the beneficial results obtained later on in the year. But for the man who runs a small shoot, and whose ground and stock are meagre, winter feeding is absolutely vital.

Every year when the weather gets hard, nature takes a toll of the old and the maimed or 'pricked' birds. This winter wastage is perfectly natural and ensures that the remaining stock is healthy. But if conditions are really bad, and particularly if cold winds persist, many healthy birds will get weak and may well die, simply from lack of food – or from having too little food with enough protein in it to sustain warmth and life in hard weather.

The later in the year that intense cold or freezing winds prevail, the greater the danger for birds already weakened by privation. Jugging as a covey in a ploughed field with an icy wind must be hell in December, but think of a pair of partridges in the same position in February. Snow is not so bad if it does not freeze

---

*November 1988 I fear that things are really going from bad to worse. Bag size which equals money and vice versa is now often the only criteria. So all the more important for a small shoot to enjoy its status. In this case small certainly equals beautiful as well as more fun and less expense.

on top – partridges will take a quick advantage of any thaw in sunny spots – but nonetheless life must be very difficult.

Pheasants seem to survive better than partridges, probably because they are armed with a pretty formidable pair of feet, and their diet is more varied. They will keep to the warm coverts in hard weather, and all you have to do is keep the feeds open, if necessary dig them out, and then keep on feeding. They know quite well where the larder is by this time.

But the poor partridges, whose winter diet consists mainly of clover or grass (most other seeds having been ploughed under long ago), are in a very different position. If the clover is covered only a little, then the warmth of their bodies will thaw the snow sufficiently to allow them to eat. But if it is two feet down it is another matter, and they do not burrow under the snow like grouse. Prolonged snow and, worse still, ice conditions soon have a serious effect on them. The winter of 1946–7 nearly fixed the stock in this country for good, though this was the last straw after a bad keeperless period due to the war. So you must do something, even if it entails icy hands and gumboots full of snow.

To anticipate really hard weather, it is wise to establish several partridge feeds in, say, late November. By this time most of the ground will be ploughed and the partridges will have become established near whatever one-year leys or permanent pastures there are. So your feeds or hoppers should be sited by observation, where you see the coveys. Try to use the sheltered side of any hedge. A rick is a good place provided it is clear of rats. But a feed made in the open is better than none at all, though once again I must warn you not to drop alien seeds on ground where they can cause trouble.

It may seem to you that the partridges hardly look at your feeds while they can get the clover. But I expect they take more than you think; and at least the feeds keep your outlying pheasants happy, and pheasants can provide an amusing drive out of the hedgerows. Moreover, when the weather goes sour, then those feeds really come into their own, provided you

Do you want this?

keep them open. By this time partridges know where they are. Nothing is more satisfactory than to see a covey pecking away at your feed, when you know that they would be hard pushed to get anything else. Tail corn, grass seeds – anything will do, scattered in shallow straw or hay off a rick or simply on the ground. The other birds will come and get it, so it pays to be generous, and no one can grudge any bird something in such weather.

Anyone who has seen how partridges will concentrate where cattle have been fed silage, hay or straw in cold weather will get the idea of what a winter feed means. When the thaw comes, they seem less than grateful and they may hardly look at the feed, but at least you have the satisfaction of knowing that they are still with you.

The second object of winter feeding is to bring your birds to the point of lay in good condition, and not half-starved. Obviously such stock is more likely to lay fertile eggs and produce sturdy

Or this?

chicks. Experiments have shown that many estates, whose nest count was satisfactory in May, were sadly distressed around about Ascot Week, when some failed to hatch at all and others came off with about three young.

Here is an idea for anyone who really wants to be kind to his partridges. Invent some sort of small burner, on the lines of those used for melting tar on the roads, which could be towed behind a Landrover or tractor. This would melt the snow on the clover and the bare patch could then be fed!

It is important that partridges nest near clover rather than actually in it – particularly if the clover is to be cut by that horribly efficient machine, the forage harvester. Of all the scourges modern farming has brought to game, this engine of destruction is by far the worst. Mr Gillette would be proud of the way it shaves the pastures, and I often tell one of my 'pigeon employers' that the real reason his cattle survive is that his silage pits are full of protein from the various animals and birds carved up inside it!

Unfortunately, partridges are very fond of clover as a winter diet; so no good at all is done by the machine to them, or to your shoot. From November on, partridges are forced to concentrate on the clover or grasses. By nesting time they are still around and will decide to make their nests in that nice long grass, only to be chopped up at the first silage cut. Those that survived, and their broods, may well get the 'treatment' when later operations take place, as silage-making seems to go on as long as there is grass to cut. Even the eggs cannot be picked up and put under broody bantams, as they are usually well scrambled. Thus it is a vicious circle.

I have heard some very harsh words from keepers on the subject, and this at present insoluble problem can make a real nonsense of your stock-count of pairs, so hopefully carried out in the month of March. People have tried 'dogging' the fields in a vain attempt to get the birds to change their quarters. The nests are almost impossible to find and it does not really work. So the only hope is to make some good nesting cover in nearby hedgerows whenever you can. Better still, leave some headlands and so draw the partridges from the leys to your winter feeds.

This Spring, thank goodness, the chances of partridges and other birds being poisoned by seed dressing are somewhat less than they used to be, provided every farmer does not see his case as 'exceptional'. The Ministry of Agriculture and Fisheries have recommended that three poisonous seed dressings should not be used except in exceptional circumstances – i.e. where a heavy infestation of nasty bugs occurs. Last year, and for many years previously, the losses to game were considerable. At the time of writing I have not heard of any recent instances of birds being found dead, which is a hopeful sign, and it looks as if the new understanding is working.

However, it is well worth finding out if your farmer *is* going to sow such dressed corn. If so, it will probably be to combat wheat bulb-fly in the autumn. In that case, feed like anything in your woods and endeavour to keep the birds off the field in question. Few people realize that quite apart from the actual deaths caused, the fertility of birds can be affected very greatly by their eating a quantity of corn dressed with one of these poisons. You can imagine how a keeper, who knows this, will wonder about those carefully nurtured nests! Will they be as successful, after all his efforts, as he, and certainly poor Mrs Partridge, hope?

Anyway, the new recommendations will make a lot of difference to the song-bird population, especially larks which have taken a terrible beating every spring sowing. The dressing did not seem to matter so much when rain washed it off the seed. But in good planting weather it was disastrous.

These moans about seed dressings were written in 1962. It was a very serious situation and I have left it in to show that it was so. Now, in 1988 things are much better and the Ministry of Agriculture's recommendations on seed dressings are pretty vigorous.

Poor partridge! At least poor partridge in my part of the world – Hampshire. In East Anglia, the winter cropping programme seems to leave a lot more cover on top of the ground. In theory this should mean a greater pair-density, as visibility is more limited. I have been surprised, though, to hear that birds do not like sugar beet. All I can say is that I wish we had some here. In this part of the world, the pair at one end of a permanent ley can see another a good way off, and partridges don't like this. Also, more and more hedgerows are grubbed out, which of course means fewer nesting sites. At the other extreme, with acres of well-sprayed, weedless, and thus insectless corn they have too much cover and precious little headland on which to take their brood when it is wet. Then along comes the harvest and – *whoosh* – in two weeks their cover has gone, though the stubbles remain. But not for long as us pigeon shooters know only too well.

This must, I think, be the best part of a partridge's life. Even for a short period, before the plough takes over, they have enough cover and food and relatively little disturbance and they always seem to look fit and well. But all too soon everything has changed, and they are back on the bare leys and what you can offer them. It is surely not too much to expect, this winter feeding; after all, it is your shoot.

This rather dismal picture was all too true in 1962, and became even worse in the winter of 1962–3 which decimated stocks of all birds, not only game. During the last year or so things have changed considerably for the better for the partridge population, as you will see under 'Partridge Problems'.

In that nasty winter of 1962–3, just after this book was first published, I learnt the hard way that pheasants must have digestive grit (granagrit) when they are being fed hard grain and when they cannot get natural grit on either frosted or snow-covered ground. I was running a big shoot in

Berkshire, and we could not understand why we found birds lying dead under the roosting trees, perfectly healthy and with full crops. I suppose they could not digest the food and had a sort of heart attack. So I now put out small piles of granagrit on bare places (and always the same places), near strategic feeds and watch them. When they disappear, top up, I am pretty certain that the reason we see so many dead pheasants on roads is the same as I have just related. So, amateur keepers, be a little professional and keep your birds alive by sensibly giving them some grit.

Come mid-March you can also put down oyster-shell grit, in the same places, hoping that Mrs Pheasant will eat it and thereby lay better and stronger eggs. They certainly do eat it, the piles are always scratched about, but I cannot prove that the eggs are in fact better quality. I would doubt, except in captivity whether it is necessary to provide grit for partridges, except in bad snow conditions, but at least it is there if they want it, and it is certainly a must, like the dusting bath places for the pheasants. Both grana- and oyster-shell grit are still relatively cheap.

The spray situation is also very much better but all in all there is no doubt that winter feeding for both pheasants and partridges is utterly vital.

Farms which are not completely manicured will support a few coveys of wild greys. But tame greys are likely to be a disaster for the local wild stock and they almost all die of 'Gapes' in the New Year. Reared Chikor/French Cross will breed if the Lord in the shape of the weather is kind. But crosses are not popular with, or actively forbidden by, the EEC. The 'set aside' policy might help. Perhaps one could hope for a few slightly weedy and therefore insect attracting fields. It is too early to say.

But I am quite certain that the Game Conservancy's 'Conservation Headlands' technique (see Partridge Problems) is the best bet. In a way it is a form of set, or at least spray aside.

WORKING IN WITH THE FARM

I HAVE already said so many rude things about the evils of modern farming in relation to game, that I hesitate to ask farmers any favours! But one thing we can agree on is that the destruction of rats is very important to both sides. Going on from there, as a shooting tenant it is an excellent idea to discuss with the farmer, or it might be with the estate office, the various ways of improving your shoot without undue inconvenience, labour or cost to either of you. Nowadays it is virtually impossible to be the tenant of a small shoot and have little or no co-operation from the man who farms it, let alone the estate which owns it.

In theory, matters should be easier for the owner-farmer who shoots his own ground, but as with many things in life people get used to the *status quo*, and fail to see even the most obvious improvements which could be made with very little cost or labour. And such owner-farmers are usually quick to stress what is quite true, that farming must come first.

There are very few partridge manors or estates left, where the farming is run essentially for the shooting. And the smaller shoot can rarely afford such luxuries as fields of specially planted kale. On the other hand, where kale is grown on the farm anyway, the odd acre planted in unproductive corners can be of great shooting value. Headlands are often poor producers and the cereal yield is so light that little is lost by planting a strip of mustard or kale instead. Moreover, the kale can be cut and carted for the cattle, and the mustard – if planted in the last week of July, as it should be – can be ploughed in in the following year and may well cause that headland to produce a better crop. I consider mustard to be the best game crop on the farm, with the sole exception of kale left for seed, but from both the farming and shooting points of view, I say, once again, plant it in the last week in July. If you put it in much earlier, it goes brittle and dry just when you need it most for cover and provides little benefit to the ground when ploughed in. But if planted later than the end of July, with a little luck and some rain and fertilizer it will still come, and provide good game cover, and later on the seed gives partridges a welcome diet in the hungry months.

I know that the drought weather in 1976 provided precious little mustard or kale in the way of game cover but what I have written still holds good for most years.

Perhaps I should now mention maize, a relative new comer to this area. Maize provides super habitat and food for both partridges and pheasants, but it is not easy to drive. Because they can run right through it, you are liable to get a fantastic 'flush' and that is that. But even the stubbles are great holders of birds and can usually be worked into something with more cover to provide more evenly spaced birds. Cross drilling, (see

Fig. 5) will help. You can also sow millet with the maize to thicken it up.

Mustard is best broadcast, though bare patches should be left, which will allow the birds to get out on 'the dry'. With an early harvest you may be able to get a small strip of stubble ploughed up and sown with mustard at the last minute, and this can be most valuable. If there is no time to plough, scuff it up, sow, and hope for the best! The Game Conservancy has been very successful in establishing mustard by hand broadcasting into standing corn two or three weeks before harvest. The humidity at ground level offers some protection from drought, but a showery day is the best time to sow.

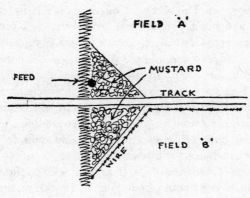

FIGURE 7

Even a small patch of half an acre provides some sort of holding cover, into which converging hedgerows can be driven and so form a flushing point. Figure 7 shows a track leading through a hedgerow. Use a few yards of headland, and scuff up the sides of the track as it goes between the hedge if there is room. Let us say field A contains autumn-sown barley, and field B on the other side of the track is a ley due to be turned over later in the year. An early harvest may make it possible to plough and harrow the small corner of field A (and incidentally don't forget to put a few bales, whilst they are still out, in the hedge beside field A, at the tactical site for your feed). If stock are still on field B, it may not be too difficult to cut off a corner for mustard by using a few posts and wire from the existing wire on the track to the hedge. But if this is too difficult, then scrap field B and use a bit more of field A. Make the feed before the mustard comes up, so that birds get used to the area and readily use the mustard as soon as it is high enough. And I have mentioned elsewhere how popular artificially made dust baths can be; this is a first-class place for one, near your hedge feed. Your reward will be quickly visible if the weather stays fine – with the little extra trouble involved you will have an extra stand and a winter feed at the same time.

My friends at The Game Conservancy tell us that seed kale pays a dividend once every five years, and turns itself over most years. Certainly it is a wonderful help on a small shoot and absolutely sure to hold your birds in the late shooting season and in the hungry months, since it is the perfect set-up for winter feeding. It will provide cover and sanctuary when the grass cutting is on and every sensible mum will have noted it down to take her young into when the surrounding corn is cut. Properly fed (and kale and mustard should definitely be fed with straw and bales for birds to sit on, or to use as a watch tower), you can await your 'first time over' with confidence! Do not be too choosey about which type of kale to use; any kale is better than no kale, though I think the smaller types such as Thousand-headed are better than Marrow-stem, which can be too tall and so too dark and dank inside. But whatever you do, if your piece is of any size, try to drill it, otherwise in a wet year you may get a tangled mass of almost impenetrable stuff which neither the pheasants nor your beaters will thank you for. If it is a big field and your farmer is co-operative (and invited to your first time over!), it would be nice to have the drills running the way you want the birds to go, and to have the last twenty yards drilled crosswise to act as a flushing point.

Very small pieces of kale can be scuffed up, sown by hand, and then raked over. It is not a bad idea, and much less exhausting, to sow half the piece one week and half the next. Different weather conditions can make all the difference to the growth. Any piece is better than nothing, but generally speaking it is sensible to have a piece big enough so that when you arrive to feed, birds run into it but do not flush. It is surprising how small a piece of kale will, in fact, hold them, especially when they get to know that your presence simply means the dinner gong. But if there is any danger of them flushing it may be wiser to feed heavily for the last time the day before your shoot and then leave it quiet. However, this is a confession of failure and should not be necessary, except possibly late in the season.

I am not all that keen on buckwheat. It is an excellent early 'draw', but it soon withers and dies back and I much prefer something that provides cover throughout the season. A little buckwheat mixed with your kale or mustard can do no harm. But I personally use a mixture of half mustard and half Thousand-headed kale. When the mustard starts to fall, or is knocked over by the wind, the kale supports it. With my hand-sowing it does not appear necessary to leave bare patches deliberately; there always *are* plenty!

The various game-crops on the market are excellent to fill in the odd corner, though I believe they should be planted very thinly as they are inclined to make rather a jungle. If the pigeons haven't eaten the lot, you can always wait until spring the following year to see if you will get another self-sown crop – which will delight the idle. A little fertilizer will help. I now think it vital to use some fertilizer with any game crop you plant. But get advice. I also sow the seed corn, peas or beans taken from pigeons' crops in any possible corner, often using the heaps of weeds from the strawberry beds. If they fail to come up, I have another go, using kale or mustard seed and if this too fails at least they become potential dusting places.

A chalkpit, or any pit for that matter, is a great help to the small shoot and much trouble should be taken to make it attractive. Because it is a pit, it is sheltered and warm, and so beloved by pheasants. Such pits are often used as dumps for old farm rubbish which attracts rats, so they must rank high on your list for routine visits by the 'rodent operator'. But another sort of rubbish, that from the drier, is also often chucked into the pit and, of course, pheasants and partridges are very partial to the weed-seeds it contains, quite apart from the corn. Except for these rare visits a pit is probably fairly quiet and undisturbed, which is another good point in its favour.

Most pits in my part of the world have a few large trees growing in them, the rest of the cover consisting of elder with a few bramble bushes growing on the rim. Now, elder is no use if left to grow into a tree; it excludes the light and even the nettle is hard put to grow under it. But it is the easiest wood in the world to cut and lay as it splits very nicely. A most excellent Sunday afternoon's entertainment in March can be had by taking an axe and a hedge-knife into your pit and proceeding to lay about you. However, reconnoitre first to spot any pheasant droppings. It would be a great pity to chop down a roosting tree or limb, and it is better to leave the surrounding trees as the roost has probably been chosen as relatively draught-proof. The general idea is to let in the sun and so allow 'white grass' and better class nettles to grow up. These catch on to the fallen trees or branches and so provide thicker nesting cover. When they die back, they still provide some cover for shooting purposes.

Depending on how thick the trees are, cut down some completely (anyone who knows how to use an axe at all can really go to town on elder), but 'lay' others cunningly so that they will live. It is easier to let the trees fall downhill, but you should cut on some sort of plan, as it is better to have bits of very thick cover consisting of several trees on top of each other, some living and some dead. Everything will die down in due course but will still leave some cover, whereas trees just cut down and left on their own simply wither away. You will obviously leave good gaps on the south and western slope so that the sun can get in. Do not be too ruthless on the east or north side and leave a good windbreak against the winter winds.

Most pits have bramble patches on the edge and if they are too thick these can be cut back to encourage new growth. Here is the place to plant *Lonicera nitida* which will grow in poor soils and whose cuttings strike very easily. It provides good evergreen cover. *Lycestria*, or the nutmeg tree, is also popular and grows easily. Another quickly spreading, covert-making shrub is *Rosa Virginiana*.

Sometimes it is possible to plant a small perimeter of kale-mustard around the pit, or if the pit is very open you could put some in by hand on the sunny slope. I have also successfully combined a pit, as cover and roosting area, with a larger piece of green stuff in the adjoining field. Thus you can blank the one into the other, whichever way goes best.

Perhaps the first step in pit conservation is to ask the farmer to fence it in against cattle. The chances are that the pit is used as a dump, and therefore it is reasonable to suppose that the farmer does not want his cattle to cut themselves on an old tin and so will be quite happy to keep them out. But if you have done a lot of cutting work in February or March when the fields around the pit in question were bare plough, and if the farmer undersows it in spring you will (as I did recently) find your nice work all trampled and bare as a result of his letting the cattle in during the autumn. And this at the very moment when you want your carefully fed pit to remain quiet.

The cunning thing to do is to persuade the farmer that the headland of the pit is highly unproductive and get him to put the fence a few feet from the edge. If the field is undersown and the fence is more or less permanent, you will get a first-class winter feed for partridges, which you can join up with the pheasant feed in the pit. This latter should be provided with straw in the usual way, with some bales both to sit on in the pit and to act as suntraps or watch towers on the edge. Dusting places should be easy to dig, and the slopes make it easier to construct one of the corrugated iron shelters I shall describe later.

If your pit is small and you come suddenly over the rim, birds do tend to flush. This is obviously one reason for providing a lot of cover which they can run into. In any case, though, it is wise to make some sort of noise to let them know you are coming, and hope that they will run away while you feed without actually leaving in a flurry. But if you are afraid of losing them, it is better to feed heavily the day before your shoot and then leave the pit quiet, praying that the farmer will not choose that particular moment to have a general clear-out.

People often make the mistake of thinking that pheasants fly badly out of a pit. They may start off a bit low, but if you stand your guns well back (at least 70 to 80 yards from the pit), they will see them and go right up. And it behoves you to see that your guns go quietly to their places.

It is often possible, and indeed better, to drive a certain area of ground, including any hedgerows, towards the pit. Thus you may get a short partridge drive, culminating in a pheasant stand from the pit itself. When your beaters approach the pit let only one or two appear on the perimeter, and tap. If you let all your beaters in together, then all the birds may flush at once. There is usually a fairly well-known line of flight and you should be able to put your guns across it, even though this may mean bringing some of them in from the flanks.

Hedgerows, if used for driving purposes, must of necessity remain fairly high unless the ground falls away very steeply. But this does not prevent you from making better nesting cover, by cutting out 'bays' and pieces out of the bottom of the hedge so that the sun can encourage young growth, grass and nettles to flourish. A buzz-saw on a movable arm attached to a tractor can do the most marvellous amount of work in a few hours if properly handled. Any money spent on the contractor for such work is well-invested. The clippings can be burnt in the hedge for dusting places, and your trouble will be well repaid when you see Mr and Mrs Partridge and family enjoying themselves in one of your 'bays'.

The art of making straggly hedges into good nesting sites pays an enormous dividend. The great danger to sitting game birds nowadays is to be cut out or silaged. Therefore the more attractive you make the hedges, the more birds will use them instead of nesting in the open – and this applies to woods as well. True, the brood may well get the chop when the field is cut again later on, but that is a chance you must take. People argue that if all the birds nest in the hedgerows they fall an easier prey to vermin. That is true enough, but it is to combat that very thing that you build your tunnel traps. And I would rather bet on the chances they take in the hedge than on the certainty of both bird and eggs being put in the 'pit' as that nasty machine shaves its way through the lucerne.

A tall scraggy hedgerow is worth very little, but a short thick one with plenty of grass and young growth can hold birds in the shooting season as well as their nests. So, open or trim it up, though take care to leave it cattle-proof if it is acting as that sort of a fence. Provided you get the all-clear from the farmer you can really please your partridges by growing little patches of white clover in the sunny open spaces in the hedgerows.

Together with the fence or hedge goes that much debated piece of ground, the headland. I have already said that headlands next to strips, or under beech trees, may not provide much cereal yield. But generally speaking, from the farming point of view, the more headland that is left the less ground grows corn. So the majority of farmers understandably plough right up to the hedge and if you do some work and cut the hedge back to allow new growth, you stand a good chance (as happened to me once) that the farmer will simply plough still further in! Not quite the same picture with 'set aside' looming. But my fear is that whether it is 'set aside' or not spraying 6 metres of headland, most farmers will really spray or cultivate the rest of their farm, human nature being what it is.

So there it is. Unless the ground is really unproductive, there is not much chance of your farmer leaving a decent headland. And I am convinced that this is one of the main reasons for the decline of partridges in this country. On the few estates where headlands are left by order, there are certainly more partridges. There are two reasons for this. Firstly, if there is a headland there is more winter food for the adults. Spraying is less likely to reach and affect the nests in the hedgerow, and will destroy less of the insect life in the area when the young hatch. Secondly, partridge pairs will not stand being too close together. With no headland they are all forced onto the leys which are bare, and they can see each other a long way off. With headlands, they can take up residence on their own little beat, and so the number of pairs per acre can be denser.

This second factor may not affect the very small shoot of a few acres, but it makes all the difference to the country as a whole and is one of the direct causes, at least in this part of the country, of the disastrous cycle whereby birds are forced onto the leys for the clover, then stay to nest nearby because the food is good, and are thus all the more likely to be chopped up. Though it may seem a bore, white clover grown in the hedges may keep the partridges away from the leys. Alternatively, try to persuade that long-suffering man, the farmer, to undersow any permanent tracks or strips with something like S100 Aberystwyth. Even if some of it gets churned up by tractors, this type of white clover is pretty tough and may survive to provide that vital winter feed. Where such strips exist, they look very nice and give the farm that well-kept look.

Have you got any pylons on your ground? If so, fence them in as they provide good nesting cover. If they are easily accessible then they are good places to put a hopper for winter feeding. The same applies to any corner where wire fences or hedges meet and which is too narrow to cultivate.

It is probably only possible to make a 'remise' or enclosure on your own ground if you can rent an unprofitable acre from the farm. This is one little bit of ground where you can make all your daydreams come true, even if only on a tiny scale. Here you can sow what you like for your birds, secure in the knowledge that no spray will touch either the crop or the insects you hope it will harbour. In that sunny corner you can experiment with a variety of dust baths if you like, and only the rain can make them even temporarily unattractive. That old drinking-fountain stands filled with fresh water (you have forgotten the permanganate of potash), ready to quench the thirst of any bird customer. And as for food, Fortnum and Mason itself could not provide a more abundant assortment, with grit to help it down. The whole area, in my 'remise', is guarded from hungry enemies by three tunnel traps as well as four Warfarin pipes.

A 'remise', which is a bit of land specially for birds, and is untouched by modern farming, should provide everything that those lucky birds could possibly wish for. Apart from the cover you plant, whether it be kale or mustard or any experimental mixture you like to dream up, the 'remise' should have a certain amount of natural cover and a few decent sized thorn bushes or Christmas trees for roosting. Branches can always be dragged in and placed in circular piles so that the grass comes up and lodges.

The only snag of a 'remise' is that you get much too fond of the 'regulars' who inhabit it (simply because they *are* regulars and so make you think you are jolly clever). This can reach such a pitch that it is absolute agony on shooting days worrying in case any of them get shot. On my second shoot I never stopped the 'remise', but, alas, my two pet cocks failed to take advantage of this deliberate omission and both got the chop. And I had put a guest who is normally a safe bet not to hit anything in the place where they usually break. Unfortunately, they had to go over dead-eyed Dick at No 3, and that was that. But they ate well, as indeed they should have done! 'Remises' are fun, but don't get too attached to them.

As mine is a good example of a really small shoot, perhaps I should tell you a little about it. The vast Coats Estate consists of fourteen acres. House and garden take up one acre, permanent leys nine acres, and there are three-and-a-half acres of Christmas trees in various stages of growth. The remaining half acre is my 'remise'. We rely on wild birds except for two coops under broodies, most of which I fear get eaten by the village cats. Our annual bag is about twenty-five pheasants. We have two shoots and I maraud some cocks. We get a few partridges, but this is a matter of luck. My neighbour is kind enough to allow us to stand guns in his field, and in all the drives (of which there are three) birds are driven off the ground. I feed it more or less all the year round, and at present have a stock of about three cocks and twelve hens.

The Ten Acre Shoot

The last paragraph which you have been reading was written in 1962. I have left it as it is so that you can see the difference which time and a little care can produce, on exactly the same bit of ground.

Well now, I suggest that you read, mark, learn, and inwardly digest the following for two good reasons. The first is that this is really what the book is all about and practically all Will Garfit's photographs and wash drawings were done on the ground here at Tower Hill. The second is that provided you budget for the years, and plan ahead, you can do exactly what we have done on a similar piece of ground.

1977 The same vast estate is now down to twelve acres as we sold two acres to pay for the daughter's schooling. Two of these remaining twelve acres are house and garden, the latter enlarged to cope with strawberry nursery, greenhouse, etc. So, as Colin Willock will tell you, we are the Ten Acre Shoot. There are about five acres of Christmas trees in assorted sizes. There is a two-acre field usually lent to my neighbour for kale, or, in latter years, maize. This field is conveniently near the road, so his cowman can cut either kale or maize and feed it straight to the cattle. And of course it helps me to keep the birds.

The remainder, apart from the 'remise' which is still about half an acre, is for our strawberry business. There are four plots and they are rotated on a two-year basis, so that there is mustard to be ploughed in as green manure on two of them and the other two have either first- or second-year plants. Between the plots is a narrow twelve-yard strip of grass and Christmas trees. There is a similar strip along the boundary. There are also two two-yard strips of buddleias which are meant to act as windbreaks for the strawberries.

Over the years the shoot has become a self-contained unit, yet the ground is commercially worked, and is by no means just a pheasant shoot. Of course there have been problems, particularly with the Christmas trees, which started off all right as a market, but then the plastic Christmas tree rather killed it. But the trade is back again now. Partly perhaps because we could not sell them, we now have some quite good 'timber', some of it thirty years old, and they produce the roosting cover for the pheasants. I feel this is very important, for if birds go to bed on your ground they can rightly be held to belong to you. They are in fact residents. So by keeping a good stock at the end of the year I have a basis for the forthcoming season. A lot will go out to nest in the surrounding hedgerows, and I am glad they do so, otherwise they may make communal nests which are no good. But I believe that in due course they will come back again, and bring their broods, back to the home comforts they know are available. Bear with me and read once again what I said in the Introduction. Treating birds right is the theme, and it is very much put into practice at Tower Hill.

November 1988 We are still the 'Ten Acre Shoot', but things have changed. First of all we are out of the strawberry business and the ground is now used for spuds. And to my fury, the bit near the road is now called the 'Nuptial Lawn' to be used for our daughter's wedding in 1989. It is normally mustard for the pheasants. The dock field situated between the 'Remise' and the main block of Christmas trees is called the dock field for good reasons. It tried to grow kale or maize, but alas defeated agronomist and knowledgeable farm manager alike, and the docks always won. Coats has had some success in broadcasting various grass seeds which seem to be winning in the bottom half. Anyway, the resident roe deer like it, and so do the pheasants, there being now a circular feed ride. I run the Landrover about five times one way and five times the other. Always on a wet day. Then some straw on top and 'sitty' bales. Idle, but it does work.

The Christmas trees are a problem and we have had to take drastic steps in February or March – cutting down whole trees to let in the light in the centre ride, and making 'numerous 20 ft × 20 ft gaps on both sides, again to let the light in and the nettles up. So there is not much vegetation under the trees, but the pheasants seem to find it warm enough and maybe they don't mind seeing a longish way – foxy loxy for instance! But we are always careful not to cut too much, lest we destroy vital roosting areas. But Mike Swan (and my Head Keeper, who will get de-moted if she's not careful) tell me that I have to do a lot more. So I can foresee a lovely argument looming!

I also put down about fifteen hens ex-laying pens every year. The poor accompanying cocks have a rough time of it with the local bosses, who of course add the girls to their harem and are probably delighted that they have had time to recover a little of their strength, it being probably the first week in June. No doubt they have been hard at it since March!*

*See Modest Rearing, *November 1988*. As we always have plenty of local 'butch' cocks I get only first week June hen pheasants nowadays. These are the 'tired ladies', and I have no hesitation in saying where I get them from. Pat Robbins of Holme Park Game Hatcheries, Wokingham, Berkshire. If you know of a 'better 'ole' etc!

Of course I get some of my neighbour's birds, and he gets some of mine. But, of the 150 shot last season his farm manager and keeper, both good friends of mine and who always help me when we shoot, could only find about thirty of his 'de-beaking Bit' marked birds. Perhaps this emphasises my belief that roosting trees must be the basis of any small shoot, because they house your birds. Further, the small shoot owner must play the game and produce as well as take.*

What then of the 'Home Comforts'? I have a lot of feeds sited in places sheltered from the various winds, which include feed-bays cut back into the Christmas trees at right angles to the main feed ride. There are different types of feed too, piles of horse manure for instance, which warm up and provide insects and a perch for Mrs Pheasant to brood her young on. Later they provide good litter.

There are three banks and two sheltered trees, and every day I kick the straw up the banks, or against the trees and feed it and every day the birds scratch it back again. The same applies to the bales. Each feed has a 'sitty' bale which serves as 'look-out', latrine and rat 'baiting point'. Pheasants like to hop on and off the bales, they like to scratch the straw away from the bales, you feed next to the bales, kick the litter back on top and they scratch it out again. Pheasants are like children, they like 'toys' and like to be amused. Such things as old corn cobs, even though there is no maize left provide good time-consuming kicking/search material. The marks made will tell you, like the barometer I have already mentioned, that they are still with you, always a constant source of worry to the small shoot owner. The bales in due course will be broken up to provide fresh litter and the small shoot must take a chance with wet straw on the birds getting '*aspergillosis*'.

November 1988 It is the fun that counts, not the bag size. Last year (1987) was a very bad wild bird year. I think we got 25 the first time. 1988 has been a better year and the three gentlemen you see with me on the back cover helped to produce 45 the first time over. They shot too well but are all involved with this book, so I forgive them.

There is also a dead leaf feed, on what my daughter calls the 'Secret Ride' beside the roosting trees.

Then there are the dusting places, some entirely made by me, others started by the pheasants and made bigger and better by me. In the first case, all you have to do is to select a warm, dry and sunny site, use your onion hoe or small spade and dig out a shallow depression. If the soil is very light and crumbly, when it dries out it may do as it is. Otherwise bring wood ashes from your fire or garden bonfire and very soon, weather permitting, you will see that your efforts have been rewarded. If it has rained but looks as if it is going to clear up, turn them over with your foot when feeding, to help them dry out. 'Service' them by bringing more ashes when required. For those started by pheasants, simply improve them by ashes or a little judicious digging.

Dust baths to game birds are what your bath is to you, so they are in fact, more than a 'home comfort' they are a necessity and an integral part of treating birds right (see photographs).

There are also a variety of watering points comprising fountains, old chicken feed troughs, pudding basins as well as the polythene 'drinkers' mentioned in 'Feeding and Tactics' (see photograph).

We have just finished cutting branches off some of the Christmas trees which in itself lets the light in and the cover grow up. I don't normally touch the roosting area trees. These branches or other artificial cover will be sited to improve those areas which I have learnt by experience to be the best flushing points. We make a sort of wigwam or shelter which will ensnare the nettles or grass when they come up. Two of these flushing points are the two strips near the strawberry beds which are farthest away from the main Christmas tree blocks. It is here too that what I call the 'afternoon' feeds, both permanent and artificial stubble are situated. Therefore the birds know all about them and when shooting we blank or run the birds into them and then fly them back again, thus showing them to their best advantage, something not always too easy to achieve on a limited acreage, and flat at that.

Some of the Christmas trees (other than the roosting trees) have got too big and so we have cut the tops off them and sold them. The remaining tree still grows and provides good cover, but has to be trimmed to let the sun in and make warm little 'remises' on their own. Topping trees was originally a Danish idea and a jolly good one too (see photographs).

Thorn bushes or elder can be cut and laid and if you have elm trees you might as well cut and lay their suckers as they will assuredly catch the beetle in due course. But you must do this sort of work in February or early March to avoid disturbing the ground in nesting time.

When feeding any small area of ground, it is wise to have one or more 'no-go' areas which are refuges into which birds can run when they hear you coming to feed, but do not flush. So such areas should be left as thick as possible. You yourself should not disturb such areas except on shooting days or when in search of predators. So think about this aspect of the small shoot, it applies just as well to a small covert on a large shoot, and your feeds can be sited accordingly.

At Tower Hill, the first drive is basically a 'blank-in' and has no feed in it but acts as a 'no-go' area. The idea is that when we start this drive most of the birds should be on the feeds and we therefore start behind them, on the boundary, and push them into the area where I want them. This ties in with my feeding arrangements on both shooting and non-shooting days. The pheasants run off into the 'no-go' area and, when I have finished feeding, return to the breakfast table. Routine on a small shoot is important. Many people ask me 'why don't you feed heavily on the day before you shoot and not on the actual day?' Apart from the collared doves, which would make a nonsense of such a plan by leaving the pheasants nothing or virtually nothing on 'D-Day', the answer to this one is that they are geared to a mobile dinner gong about 8.30 am, and though I seldom see any when feeding (they are in the 'no-go' area), I know very well that they come back on the feeds as soon as I have got out of the way. So one hopes they are where I want them to be when we start the first drive and this seems to work out in practice, the first drive being not merely a 'blank-in' but often a 'blank'!

Other parts of the ground, such as the strips serve as mini 'no-go' areas. It is extraordinary how birds will learn to move off into quite a small bit of cover, knowing that you will not go near it. You are often liable to flush birds in a small bit of game cover or strip of kale, when feeding. The 'no-go' area theory should be taken into account when siting the feeds in such areas. Anyway my ladies were often picking strawberries right through October and no doubt birds don't worry too much about *vox humana* and on ten acres surrounded on two sides by village, they jolly well can't.

As the end product of our season's work, during the late February 1977 rabbit shoot we counted about thirty hens and far too many cocks on the ground. There are also three if not four pairs of partridges, a duck still sitting and one hatched. In addition, there are too many surviving collared doves and a host of various small birds, all taking advantage of the Coats bounty.

Many generations ago, a relation of mine had a good grouse moor. A young officer was asked to shoot, and in one drive dropped a bird close to his host's butt. At the end of the drive his host was about to pick it up when his guest approached and said, 'Excuse me, Sir, I think that's one of my birds,' to be met by a basilisk glare and the rejoinder, 'On this muir, young man, they're a' ma birrds.'

So the small shoot will do well to keep a large stock of hens. And as far as my own are concerned, with all the mod. con. provided, I reckon they are 'ma birrds'.

Though woodlands probably come under the estate office, rather than the farm, their correct upkeep is most important to the welfare of any shoot, and the smaller the shoot the more important it is to make them attractive. Woodlands nowadays quite rightly have to provide an income whatever the type of timber grown. How much you, as tenant of the shoot which includes woodland, can do to improve them from the shooting point of view depends on private arrangement with the owner. But at least you can, and should, know what the estate forestry plan is. I knew a man who took a small shoot on a five-year lease, and in the third year, just when he had built up a nice stock, they clear-felled his main covert without letting him know. Needless to say, this did not help his relations with the agent concerned. In the same way you might want to make a feed for reared birds in a certain ride. It is better to learn beforehand that they intend to coppice the adjacent woodlot.

But let us hope that the small shoot will not have these problems, since a tenant is probably on good terms with the boss, or he would not have the shooting. So, provided you have permission to do some work, let us get on with it.

To start with, there are few perfect woods which require little or no attention. And if they are perfect now, they won't be in three to five years' time. But there are an enormous number of woods, or woodlots within woods, which with a little trouble can be made much more attractive to birds.

If you were to ask a pheasant what it wanted in the way of home comforts in a wood, I think it would reply, 'Light and shade, thick and thin, good warm roosting cover, and not too much of any of them all in one block, please.' What do *you* require? You presumably want to drive your pheasants, and you also want them to fly well. But almost more important still, you want to be able to keep them around.

All drives will be much the same in principle, in that the birds should run into a main flushing point from the feed which is sited between this flushing point and the beaters. So the feed must be open and preferably sunny; and the adjacent flushing point must be thick so that the birds can get into it, but it must not be a jungle or the beaters won't get through it and the birds won't get up. You also want some nice brambly patches the whole way through the wood, to flush a few early birds as the beat goes on. These will often fly rather well. And, frankly, you don't mind if a few break out, since they will be there for next time and it is good for the stock. But generally speaking you want a rather thin area at the start of the beat so that the birds can run towards your flushing point.

Finally, and optimistically, you want a good bare space of about forty yards between the flushing point and the ride where your guns are, if this is a stand in a wood. Otherwise your birds may not be very exciting. And for the same type of stand you want that ride to be at least twenty feet across and the trees behind cut back another twenty feet. (Can't you hear the agent laughing?) If this is a stand where the birds are driven from a wood over a field, then you want a good thick hedge and the trees cut back ten yards from the edge of the wood so that late birds (those that have walked through the flushing point) can rise over the hedge and not run through it to shame you. Oh! yes, you want roosting cover all right, but if given half a chance they will roost near the feed. So long as there are some warm dormitory trees, it doesn't much matter where.

'Why on earth do you want the ride so wide?'

'Well, I thought we might rear a few next year, and old Tom won't use anything but broodies, so we must have light and sun for the coops when they are put into the covert. Next year we may blank this bit of wood into that bit of kale you promised me in the five-acre, and then bring it back. But this year the guns must be able to see to shoot, even if what they shoot at is only a pigeon. And if we hit the ride a good crack now, it won't require doing again for some time. '

All this may sound Utopian, and everything cannot be done at once, but a plan that works in with the general estate programme must pay a dividend. Remember that birds don't seem to mind work going on in a wood. It may be advisable to have a feed at some point which may hold them while the work is going on, but they will quickly return home.

So if the block is too thin and dark and damp, have a bit coppiced. From the second to at least the fourth year of life, newly-coppiced wood should be good holding and flushing ground. It is better to contract out to an expert. (Watch where he has built his fires – you will see the first year how much birds love to dust in ashes.) If he won't look at it ('Too far gone, that is') try to sell some for logs and, if the farm or the estate want timber, ask them to cut it there. If all else fails, but permission is granted, another of those Sunday afternoons with an axe and bill hook can make several twenty feet by twenty feet clearings. As long as the light gets in, you will soon get brambles and/or bracken. Stagger these clearings across the line of advance of the beaters.

One keeper I know, who is now retired, had a very prolific stand near his house. This was a long strip about seventy yards wide. Unfortunately for him, the birds' line of flight was more or less straight down the strip. So, numbers 3, 4 and 5 guns had all the shooting – which was not at very high birds at that. He solved this by cutting out twenty feet by twenty feet flushing points all the way down and making a sort of barricade with the wood on the front and side of each, over which the birds had to fly. This made them rise quicker in the air. They saw the guns sooner and so spread out and altogether flew much better.

I hate the idea of wire netting or sewelling. There may be places where it is unavoidable, but it is artificial and must at least be sited so that the guns can't see it. There is nothing more awful than seeing a lot of pheasants, packed behind some netting, being unwillingly prodded into flight.

I am much more sold on the siting and composition of a number of flushing points which eventually lead up to the main flushing area. But it is sometimes almost beyond belief how perfectly normal hosts (and keepers too) who want their birds to be shootable, place their guns far too close to a covert or kale field on perfectly 'straight at 'em' stands. On a partridge drive, site your pegs right against the hedge so that they give the distance between the guns, who will presumably be in a straight line. Then the host can stand as far back as he thinks correct and the others 'dress' on him. But in a pheasant stand, where guns may not be in a straight line, I like the peg to denote the exact place where each is to stand and therefore these pegs must be sited individually and with some care. Ride shooting is more difficult. There is nothing much you can do about it, except, as I have already said, to have nice big, wide rides, with a reasonable field of fire.

You are obviously not going to have many Sunday afternoons free, but when your cover is really thick, as it so often is, beater rides can be cut in a reasonably short time. Collect some of those young gentlemen who are so keen to shoot your birds later on, arm them with a bill hook or slasher apiece, line them out as beaters and tell them to appear at the other end! Another idea, which a friend of mine puts into practice with success, is to use a rotavator behind a good powerful tractor. This can only be done if there are not too many tree stumps around (though you can often see these in time to avoid them), and it works best if you have a scout walking in front. It is surprising how much can be achieved in a few hours and, once done, the lanes can be easily kept open.

There are also various excellent tools on the market for the purpose of clearing brambles and scrub if they get too much out of hand. One thing is certain: impenetrable brambles or thorn-cover are disliked as much by pheasants as by your beaters. To run birds into such a place, in the fond hope that it is your flushing point, is madness. If they do get up they can't fly, and I often wonder how many are imprisoned for good by the beaters' boots. It is better in this case to run your birds from the thick to the thin. By doing so, you may at least see some of them. But all things in a wood are temporary. Nature will have her way; in due course the secondary growth will gradually thin out the brambles, and in a year or so you will be back where you started, thinning out those twenty foot squares and letting the light in and the brambles up again.

The Game Conservancy are very keen on woods being kept in good habitat condition, and above all, 'breaking the umbrella', so that the light can get in and make things grow. There are one or two shoots I know which are blessed with wide hedgerows, sometimes with a track or 'drove' in between. If some of the young keepers I can think of would get busy with a bill hook and make a few 'wigwams' or other cover bits to prevent the wind or the eye from reaching one end to the other, they would be well employed.

With modern flail mowers hedge trimming and maintenance has become cheaper, especially since there is no need to collect up and burn the trash. Many agriculturalists would now say that it is cheaper to maintain a hedge than to replace it and maintain a fence. The Game Conservancy's newly revised booklet No. 15, *Woodlands for Pheasants*, contains a wealth of information on woodland management, from how to plant a new spinney which qualifies for Grant Aid to how to encourage cover in a bare wood.

IMPROVING YOUR PROSPECTS

I HAVE already explained how you make dust baths with some ashes from your garden fire. If you want to make a more permanent shelter, you roof in the site which has already been dug out, with three sheets of corrugated iron. One end of each sheet is laid on the ground and kept firm with sods. The other end is supported by, and nailed to, posts driven into the ground. The height from the ground of the raised sheeting should be about three feet. It is preferable that the shelter faces south. Then it becomes a sun-trap and is more protected from the prevailing rain–wind. Game birds can be fed in these dusting shelters, though they quickly have to share their table with lots of other small birds who think that dusting and good food go well together.*

These shelters are often used in bad weather as refuges and are ideal as winter feeding points. A good raking from time to time will do no harm and keeps the soil at its best. You can often get old corrugated sheets fairly cheap at a builder's yard and the posts should cost you nothing. The sight of a pair of partridges dusting side by side, or an old cock really getting down to his bath, will amply repay you for your trouble.

I think you have to experiment with the siting of these shelters. Partridges and pheasants seem to like some, but don't take to others, for no apparent reason. But dusting places or shelters definitely pay dividends and their value will come to be more and more respected.

November 1988 Your main problem will be bunnies, who find the soft soil just the job for holes. I don't think it matters much.

I have already said something, under Feeding and Tactics, about water points. There are two schools of thought about the provision of water for birds. Many keepers think that it is unnecessary and even wrong to provide it. Adult partridges, they say, always drink from the dew or get moisture from the leaves or grass they eat; and the chicks find sufficient moisture in their insect food, at least until they are old enough to follow their parents' example. Pheasants, these keepers will tell you, get water from the dew, a cattle trough or the base of a beech tree, or somewhere, and in their case it is dangerous to put out water as it can give them some foul disease if it stays too long in the sun (though a little permanganate of potash added to the water apparently solves this problem). Lastly, young pheasants are such foolish birds that they won't know how to get water naturally if the artificial supply dries up for any reason. The Eley Kynoch Game Research Station did not recommend putting out water at all, except for reared birds, but after our experiences in the 1976 drought summer I bet they do now, in their new guise as The Game Conservancy.

Wild pheasants will certainly empty fountains or old half tyres, in fact anything that is put out for them. Reared birds must definitely have plenty of fresh water even when put out to covert. But that is part of the normal drill.

So, on a very small shoot, particularly one devoid of accessible natural water, I suggest it is worthwhile putting out one or two permanent fountains or polythene sack drinking places. They definitely help to keep the birds about. I do not think that nowadays, after more experience on watering problems it is enough to rely on the dew until this fails (which is rare, but has happened several times in the last few years) and then think seriously about providing water straight away. Old tyres cut in two, placed under a tree with an old bit of corrugated iron laid so as to catch the rain, hold water for quite a period and can salve your conscience. A lot will depend on local conditions. Forestry land, for instance, can get very dry in summer and birds may well need some help. It is obviously sensible to put your water near a feed which they already know. But put it in the shade.

Dogs

Your small shoot is not complete without a dog, nor will you ever get the same satisfaction or, indeed, results without one. To start with, it is only fair to your dogless guns to have an animal which will pick up runners during and after a shoot, and on small hedgerow days your dog will put up those old cocks which no beater can dislodge.* He will enjoy his day, and so will you, and a little wildness is no great sin provided he doesn't course that hare clean through the next beat. And in very thick cover, whether it be kale or brambles, it is surely better to hunt a dog and put up birds even if they go the wrong way, than have your beaters struggle through it with nothing to show for their efforts.

November 1988 If we only had a few 'Dudleys' – Colin Willock's Worst Dog in the World. He is the boy for the brambles. Get Colin's newly published '*The Complete Dudley*' (Tideline). You won't regret it.

Training a young dog needs time, but natural conditions and game or pigeon shooting give you an enormous advantage over those who have only the lawn. However, if for any reason you cannot keep a dog, and your guns on any particular day are also dogless, remember that there are always people who are quite happy to come out and pick up with or without a fee. There is nothing more awful than the feeling that you have left wounded birds running about.

Beware of letting a dog run loose. Game is scared by a hunting dog and in the nesting season, you, or worse still your neighbour, can have a disaster if this hunting becomes a habit.

Perhaps it is as well to signpost your land if you suffer from trespassers or their dogs. This may also discourage would-be poachers, as presumably where there is a sign saying 'Game Preserved', there is some attempt made to preserve it. Or are you merely advertising the presence of game? No one wants (or at least I don't) to stop perfectly innocent people from enjoying the countryside, courting or picking the odd bluebell. In today's conservation-minded climate many people do respect requests to keep their dogs under control, especially on nature reserves. The Game Conservancy's shop is able to supply 'conservation area' signs to be posted in gateways and alongside footpaths.

Difficult Ground

I help run a shoot, part of which is very open arable land with about four hedges on around 300 acres. There is only one small spinney by a much-used barn and every single one of the hedges is a public right of way and bridle path. There are few pheasants on this bit of the ground but in the last two years there have been quite a lot of grey partridges. It is amazing to me how the partridges get away with it despite the hordes of people who walk there, many of them with dogs, not to speak of the horses, including a riding school.

I winter feed the hedges and the spinney, there is nowhere else to do it. And as I have already mentioned this is where I had to make the polythene drinkers last year. It is probable that the partridges nest in the open, perhaps helped by direct drilling, oil-seed rape and winter wheat, but anyway it highlights the fact that you can have a partridge shoot on a rather unpromising bit of ground, if you do the best you can for them. Perhaps this is another reason for putting your money into rearing some partridges, as opposed to pheasants only, especially when some of your shoot is more the classical type of ground favoured by partridges. A re-think is now necessary on this subject, because a vast acreage all over the country can be seen to hold partridges which only a few years ago were in drastically short supply. 'On the way out,' people said, but they were wrong.* See also 'Partridge Problems'.

Poachers

Poachers are a problem now as always. No one minds the chap who goes out occasionally for a bird for the pot. In his own way he is a sportsman although he breaks the law. And many of us would do well to search our youthful memories before casting too many stones! Unfortunately, what with high wages and the 'telly', his sort seem to be dying out, and the profit-seeking gang or the lorry driver with his gun in the cab are on the increase. And when they know that there is no full-time keeper on the ground, they are obviously more liable to pay you a visit. A rising moon coinciding with a weekend provides the most likely time, but with a gang you can never tell. If you think there is anything going on, get the police at once. If the police can get the poachers 'in

November 1988 I fear they were partly right on manicured farms, but not on those where there are unsprayed rough bits or hedges.

possession', the law will deal fairly severely with them and the weapon will probably be confiscated. And any owner or lessee of a shoot should acquaint himself with the laws of arrest and particularly with what he personally may or may not do himself. It is all rather tricky, and the nearest police station will tell you all about it.

At the start of the season let it be known as widely as possible that you have some arrangement with the police, particularly as regards patrol cars. The grapevine in the pub may do the rest. You can put black cotton across the rides, and if it is broken you know someone has passed, though it doesn't prove anything. You should know the areas where your birds roost, then see if the droppings are fresh, and look for those tell-tale feathers. But all these things are rather 'closing the stable door' and your own intelligence service (and a reputation for unbridled savagery!) are much the best safeguards as far as local operators are concerned. Against the gang coming from a long distance you are much more vulnerable.

Another insurance against poachers for the small shoot owner or renter who does not live close to his ground, is the help of farm workers or whoever helps him with the shoot chores. Hopefully they live somewhere near by. In return for carrying a gun and the sort of 'perks' mentioned later in 'Running the Shoot', it is not too much to ask that they alert the police, off their own bat, if they think something is going on. They should ring you up too, of course. But if you live ten miles away it is probably too late. So make certain that they know the local police constable personally and his telephone number, and that of the local main police station.

Pigeons

As you are the shooting tenant you have the first right to have a go at the pigeons,* but if you are not keen or lack the time, the farmer can do it himself or designate 'his man to carry the gun'. It is only fair to have them shot when they are doing damage to valuable crops, and some agreement can usually be arrived at without worrying too much about the rules and regulations.

You want to know how much pigeon shooting affects game? Well, even if the rest of this book is utter nonsense, you can take it from me, in 1962, 1977 and now in 1988, as a professional pigeon shooter that static pigeon shooting from a hide over decoys has NO harmful effect upon game; whereas walking about, shooting casually, can have a harmful effect, particularly late in the season. When shooting from a hide, I often go out to tidy up the decoys and put more out, and there are the pheasants happily feeding in the same field as I am shooting. They look up as I go out and may even move towards the hedge, but whenever I return to the hide they resume feeding. Obviously, nobody expects to decoy pigeons for some days before his first time over (though I doubt if it would do much harm). And if the ground is small, to shoot pigeons just before a cock shoot would be foolish.

Roosting is another matter and the small shoot should keep its woods quiet until the end of January. You yourself may have finished shooting by 15th January, but your neighbour may not. On large estates with many woods it would not matter except to the actual woods shot. But under no circumstances should roosting birds be disturbed during the season. I have shot pigeons in a wood and, as I was packing up, clearly heard pheasants going up to roost without bothering about me at all. But in the shooting season I would not like to chance it. Anyway, it is far better to stop shooting pigeons coming in to roost in time both to let pheasants go up and to ensure that the pigeons will continue to use that particular wood. Lastly, if a pigeon shoot is organized in your area try and co-operate by having your woods manned.

*In *Pigeon Shooting*, also published by André Deutsch, the same author deals with the whole subject of pigeon shooting.

Flight Ponds

It is surprisingly easy to make a flight pond and even easier to abuse it. In 1961 I went down to East Kent to shoot partridges and, we hoped, to flight duck on the marshland stubbles. But some 'gentlemen' (and I rather pointedly use the inverted commas) had this one well thought out. They had one or two ponds up on the downs and had plastered them with barley by the sackful. From 1st–5th September there was a cannonade every evening, and we heard that some of those taking part were using two guns. No duck were reared.

Well, my idea of the use of a flight pond is not that sort of massacre of young duck, and I am sure that the great majority of those who read this will agree. A flight pond is a rest cure. It is something to really enjoy; use it with the greatest care so that you do not mar that lovely period of day's ending when your eyes for once become the servant of your ears and you can just sit and listen in. To be fair to the duck, I do not think that a flight pond should be shot more than six or seven times a year: twice in September, perhaps, and once a month until the end of the season.

Basically a flight pond can be made in any area normally inhabited, or flown over, by duck. But there are certain places sometimes a goodish way from a fly-way which are visited by duck at night. These you must ferret out from the locals, but you can always tell whether duck are regularly using a pond or any stretch of water by the preening feathers on the bank and the dibbled state of the mud at the edge. Duck only need about twenty yards by fifteen yards of clearish water to land on. They like a nice shallow depth, at least on the edges, so that they can up-end and search for food. All-important is an easy sloping bank so that they can get out to preen without undue exertion.

Rushes or cover are not vital for a flight pond. Perhaps I should have said earlier that duck like to rest during the day and feed at dusk, or later if there is a moon. Thus, whereas the 'sea duck' seek nice safe mud banks, or even the open sea as a day refuge, their inland cousins sit in some secluded rest spot, usually with very thick cover and shade around it, or in the middle of a reservoir. But one and all flight at dusk to the various feeding places, and your flight pond is simply an artificial feeding place. So if you can find a small pond, or it may be a backwater which answers more or less to the specifications outlined above, and if you feed it regularly, the chances are that duck will find it in their nocturnal rambles.

Trying to grow seed-bearing plants for duck is not always successful, but there are several things you can do to make your pond more attractive; they are great fun to do, but you will need a pair of thigh waders. You can stake out a bale or two of straw in the water for them to sit on. If you encase them in wire netting they last longer; or you can drive in two posts and lash a straight tree trunk to them. If your pond is too deep you can make a plank raft which floats just beneath the surface. Attach five-gallon oil drums to each corner. These must have a watertight bung in place of the usual metal cap. By allowing sufficient water to enter the drums and then replacing the bung, you can arrive at the correct depth for the raft; and you then anchor it with stakes driven in. You use the raft for a feed, knowing that only duck can get the sunken grain. But you must be ruthless with moorhens or coots, and get rid of them. Perhaps I should stress that all these additions to your flight pond should be sited off the 'runway' for obvious reasons.

If the bank is too high or steep, a little spade-work will soon make it easier for the duck to clamber out and also ensure the correct dibbling depth at the edges. Anything from three to six inches will do. This you feed with old barley tailings or a mixture of barley and wheat. Old potatoes, etc, are, no doubt, all right, but if a duck won't eat barley it won't eat anything. Whatever you do, feed just under the water or other birds will soon find it.

After 48 hours or so, come again and see if the feed is still there. If the mud is disturbed and you can't see any feed, and if there are a few preening feathers, you can get wildly excited if you like. But come down before dusk, without a gun, and just

sit and watch which way they come in and how, at least with that wind, they approach the pond.

Then, you can build a hide – for preference so that you can shoot towards the fading light, where you can see them better. Hides can be made of hurdles or netting, or you can dig yourself a hole and put a barrel in it if you want to pretend you are on a salting. But build something lowish with a seat in it. Your skyline is much improved when sitting down, and if you can keep quite still and look through the cover in your hide they will not see you (pigeon shooters please note).

Well, I hope you enjoy your first visit because maybe you will decide to go easy on them when you first shoot. Thereafter, it depends on your observation of how your feed goes and on your conscience, as to how often you shoot. But for heaven's sake shoot only when there is a good wind. Shooting time is limited anyway and incoming birds hear the shot too easily (though you may not have seen them) and turn away. I, personally, do not believe that the moon has much to do with flight-pond shooting. If the duck are used to your menu they should come in as the light goes, or even before in wild weather. The same reasoning applies to the use of decoys. If the birds are going to come anyway, what is the use of putting out decoys?

I know one pond (about two acres) which was man-made by erecting two dams at either end of a piece of ground which was liable to flood anyway. The feeder stream comes in at the bottom, and the water backs up through a deepish drain and then spreads out. In this area were planted a lot of black and white sallies or alder. These have now grown and rushes and grass have come up. It was necessary to fence the perimeter to keep the sheep out, and the pond has now become a sort of dual rest-and-flight pond. There is a snag in this, as we found out. The pond was fed, the feed all went and we thought that the next Friday evening would be right if the wind held. Unfortunately, we forgot to come down and put the duck off at midday, with the result that they were all happily sitting in the drain or rushes when we arrived. As it was, a surprising number came back. But it is a point to remember that you must keep this sort of dual-rôle pond clear of duck during the day, if you are shooting that evening.

Wild duck are easy to rear, and this is one way in which you can repay the local duck population for your sport. The best thing to do is to join, if you are not already a member, The British Association of Shooting and Conservation, many of whose affiliated clubs are doing great work in keeping the duck population topped up. Their new address is: Marford Mill, Rossett, Wrexham, Clwyd LL12 0HL. Ringing the birds will help you to find out where they have got to. You will not shoot them all yourself, but that is no good reason not to rear any! How to make flight ponds and rear duck is best explained in The Game Conservancy Booklet 3.

MODEST REARING

BY virtue of their size, small shoots are rather prone to the suspicion that the birds shot are not always their own. This is probably quite unfounded and can be most annoying when you have taken the trouble to look after your own wild birds. Still, there it is, and perhaps the small shoot's best way of keeping on good terms with 'brassier' neighbours is to rear some pheasants, even if it is only a token number. Having done so, you are in a much stronger position and, within reason, can feed where you like in order to keep your own birds at home. I have explained my own problems, and luckily in my case they are not problems at all, in what I have written about the Ten Acre Shoot under 'Working in with the Farm'.

You must have some cover for your reared birds to use as home, though it is surprising how little the minimum can be. Nor is it absolutely necessary to have a wood or roosting cover. Many birds, particularly on downland, jug from the start in kale or mustard and never go up at night. Probably some of them have never even seen a tree. I know they used to jug in my young Christmas trees when, apart from one thorn bush, there were no roosting trees. As a result, although the village cats took their toll, at least I was safe from any night work by local characters. And the risk of poaching can be one of the great problems of rearing on a small acreage. There is bound to be a concentration of birds in any one roosting area, and this area is probably limited anyway. So if the local grapevine 'sounds' too loudly, a small shoot like this may be in for a shock. On the other hand, a man with two grass fields and a little hedgerow between them is unlikely to hold his birds for long, as his neighbours are bound to have some more exciting cover.

It is difficult to suggest a minimum acreage for the size of your ground before you embark on any rearing adventures. Birds must have a warm home, and within it roosting or jugging facilities. They should have at least one field, for preference all round the perimeter of their base, where they can 'get out of the house' and feed in the open. (You cannot stop them doing this, however hard you feed them in a covert, like us they are inclined to think, at least some of the time, that the food elsewhere tastes better.) And these fields you must control, even if you only have permission to blank them in. Much the best answer is to have one wood or home base and one kale or game mixture field, so that the birds can work happily between them. This fits in with their natural inclination to wander. Reared birds rather like routine, and if from an early age they find that there is always food in one place not too far from their living quarters, they keep on going to get it.

With ideal conditions you can have a very good shoot on a very small bit of land. You are probably bored stiff by reading about Tower Hill the Ten Acre Shoot, so to underline my suggestion that you, too, can do it, let me tell you of a friend who has a similar bit of ground. He has a garden, two small woods and a strip, all of which are very warm and well planted and were always very popular pheasant resorts in the days when he owned the adjoining land. The whole area is not more than twelve acres. Every spring his old keeper finds about twenty nests on this ground, and the annual bag is about 100–120 pheasants, which is remarkable. The extraordinary thing is that there are always more pheasants, particularly hens, at the end of the season than at the beginning. Rumour has it that my old friend, the keeper, has a magic potion with which he anoints his feed, and, as I have said, the cover is wonderfully warm. Rearing is carried on nearby; but I have found precious few tagged birds in the bag, and I think that those who breed there wander off to see the world because there is no corn, but come back as soon as they feel the urge for home-cooking and comfort. I am a great believer in the old theory that the hen will bring her brood back to where she herself was born.

With a concentration of nests per acre like that, there is no need to rear provided you look after the vermin side of things, which is not too difficult on twelve acres. But others may not be so lucky, and the decision to rear or not must depend partly on the likelihood of your holding your birds and partly on your idea of your duty to your neighbour.

Once you decide to have a go, you are faced with a variety of problems. First and most important of these is, in plain English, the question of who is to do all the work? Whatever method of rearing you adopt, someone has to be more or less on the spot pretty continually for the first 48 hours, and later at least twice a day while the birds are young. And the poults have to be regularly fed and watered when they are put to covert.

The next problem is expense. This depends on the method you use, but obviously the first question is how many birds are you going to rear? If the answer is anything up to fifty, then without doubt the best method is three broody hens, in the back garden or on the lawn. This usually means that one's wife is in charge, which is an excellent way, for the idle-minded, of having one's cake and eating it. (Needless to say, this is the way I used to work it.) For anything from 50 to 200 birds you are well advised to study the brooder system; most units will look after lots of 100 to 120. For anything above 200, I reckon you cease to be a small shoot and your labour problems and expenses will hit you a very nasty crack.

Let me say at once that I am no expert on these matters, and you will do far better to study Game Conservancy booklets Nos. 5, *Egg Production and Incubation,* 8, *Pheasant Rearing and Releasing,* or get advice from a keeper. All I intend to do is to tell you what equipment you need for both methods, and the sequence of events. I am quite prepared to be shot down on all of this; no doubt it could be done much better. But at least we have produced some pheasants with each method. Some people have 'green fingers' for this sort of thing and some haven't, and you must really find out for yourself the hard way.

If you are going to use your own eggs under broody hens, it is better to start early and to pick up the eggs from wild nests which are sited in dangerous places. In this way you will probably get all you want quite quickly, and your wild bird will be able to get on with her own job without any more interference. This also minimizes the danger of using eggs which have already been sat on. Keep your picked-up eggs flat in an egg tray with the pointed ends all facing one way; every evening turn them right over so they face the other way. Keep in a cool place; they are quite all right for ten days but it is best to set them as soon as you can. If you do find a cut-out nest later on, where the eggs have obviously been incubated, you have to put them under a broody jolly quick before they cool, and hope that she takes to them.

But I suggest, if you can afford it, that you buy your eggs from a recognized game farm. They cost about £40 per 100.

The method of catching up hen pheasants and penning for egg production is hardly for the small shoot. Good broodies are hard to find. The old barnyard hen is best if she is not too heavy. Battery hens are often rather 'skitey' and inclined to go off the brood and get hysterics – usually both together, and always when there is no replacement! Bantams are best for partridge eggs. All should be dusted with some poultry insecticide before being introduced to the nest.

You need one coop per broody, which you can knock up if you are a do-it-yourself fiend; otherwise they cost a lot. The portable units are excellent, combining both run and coop. Ordinary coops must be equipped with a movable hatch on top and you must also be able to take out the middle bar in front, at will. They must also have a shutter which fits firmly in front of the bars with no chinks at the sides from which devilish baby chicks can escape. Each coop must have a wire-netting run which should be as long as you can conveniently make it and should fit tightly against the coop, the heights being about equal. The run should have a wide removable hatch at the end nearest the coop; or leave a decent gap which can be covered with something with a brick on it! Bricks are wonderful things for this job, and it is extraordinary how many we use for some purpose or other connected with coops.

Now, to work. Make a shallow saucer-like depression in level ground (never mind about the lawn – it will be ruined anyway) and fill it with nice dry hay. Then set the coop on top, making sure that the sides are flush with the ground – otherwise a rat may do the lot in. Cover any holes with boards and supporting bricks. Put up to sixteen eggs in each nest (fewer for a small bird). It does not matter much how you arrange them; if your broody 'takes' when you introduce her she will arrange them to her liking. No doubt the cunning thing is to sit the broody for 56 hours on some dummy eggs and then change over. In any case, putting her into the coop is a moment of truth, and if she shrieks with horror and tries to get out you had better get another bird. Anyway, shut her in firmly for 24 hours and hope for the best.

The expert keeper raises the hatch to lift or ease the broody off the nest, when she comes off for her punctual morning constitutional. She is then tethered by the leg to a stick permanently stuck in the ground. When she has eaten her grain, gritted, drunk, and done her job, he puts her back and shuts the hatch. It is important that she should scour, or she fouls the nest – a little squeeze may help. In this way you do not need a run until the chicks hatch. Unfortunately, my coops are not in their first youth and are by no means watertight, so the roofs have old groundsheets fixed permanently on top and weighted with yet more bricks. This entails taking the shutter off and removing the centre bar and oozing her off the nest. But usually a broody gets into the routine, and when she sees a bit of grain in the run she comes off quite happily. When she has finished you may have to help her back, but good broodies go back of their own accord. You then shut her in again. If the

Hopper for winter feeds and storage bins handy.

Polythene drinker – essential in hot weather.

Privet cut and laid – the more habitat the better.

'Topped' spruce, the actual tops were sold as Christmas trees.

Brick tunnel trap with lid removed.

Fox wire – ask the experts for advice.

Man-made dustbath – an essential 'home comfort'.

Corrugated iron dusting shelter cum winter feed.

weather is very hot she must have ventilation and so must the eggs. So you may have to keep the shutter partly open, and provide some shade. In any case she should not be off for more than ten to fifteen minutes. The eggs *must* be warm when she goes back.

To avoid frantic memory searchings it is wise to write the whole programme out in advance so that you know exactly when things are meant to happen. About the ninth day, you should damp the eggs with warm water to soften the shell. Some coops have wooden bottoms and we have to make our nests on these. This is quite all right, but you may have to start damping the eggs a bit more freely. Sprinkling with a watering can on the ground outside will help if it is very hot. Continue this damping once every second day until the eighteenth day, when you give them a bit more. On the morning of the twenty-third day to the twenty-fourth day (when they are due to hatch) you should not let her off at all, and in many cases she shows no inclination to leave the nest, perhaps knowing she is near her time!

At last the great day arrives. The one thing not to do is to keep on peeking to see if there are any cheeps. Leave her quiet and look in the morning. If she has not finished hatching let her be; the chicks will not starve. By now your run will be in position, and I repeat once again – make sure it fits tightly against the coop and lies flush with the ground; otherwise put up more barricades or the little perishers are sure to escape. The pastime of rescuing chicks from herbaceous borders is not to be recommended.

By now, too, you will have bought your pheasant-chick starter-crumbs and grit. Starter-crumbs now cost about £350 per ton and growers slightly less. Give and take, one ton of each does about a thousand chicks. Therefore you can cost out each chick until it goes into covert in seven weeks at about 75p. Use starter-crumbs for about the first three weeks and grower-pellets thereafter. On the other hand a brace of pheasants in 1987 was worth about £3 off the shoot. In 1988 massive rearing has already reduced the price to £1.50 a brace. Not funny for the small shoot. So you must take that into account, and don't forget you can always do things cheaper on a limited scale and on a do-it-yourself basis. Your capital investment will not run away.

As soon as the broody has finished hatching and the chicks have dried off, open the shutter and entice them with some crumbs. When they see the old woman take a peck or two, the babies quickly get the idea. As soon as they can feed, try to entice her out to feed and water and scour. She will herself teach them to drink, but a beak or two shoved in the water for slow starters does just as well.

While she is busy, clean up the broken eggshells, etc, and put in some fresh hay, but not too much or the chicks may get caught up in it and then smothered. Then let her go back with them, put in a few crumbs and shut up for the night. Weather permitting (you can always cover the run with sacking) remove the shutter to let them run in and out, and provide permanent food and water in easily get-at-able containers. Let her off as usual; broodies must be content with pheasant crumbs until about the third week, when the chicks can have some kibbled, or small, wheat. The foster mum can thus teach the chicks to scratch.

The run and coop must be moved from time to time to fresh ground. As the chicks grow bigger, it is essential to give them more room, and you must either let them into a bigger run or join two runs together with popholes. The advantage of their being on a lawn is that they get a certain amount of grass and clover and are safer from enemies. But anyway, they should have some green stuff as toys hung from the roof of the run, and it is important to give them a sun shelter if it is very hot. Feather-pecking is less likely with small numbers, but space is the determining factor.

After the end of the sixth week you must move them into their home, which may be a kale field (remember to ensure that it is planted at the right time so that there is enough kale to receive them), or it may be that nice sunny ride we have mentioned. It is far better to take mum too, coop and all. She acts as an anchor when, after about ten days, you take the runs away. You can also let some of the broodies out to pick about. Stagger some of the releases so that the whole thing takes about two weeks. If some of the early 'escapees' learn to roost quickly, they may teach the others. Needless to say, you will have made a feed wherever the coops were placed and probably 'stop feeds' at all the likely exits. Water will also be laid on, and here a large container of some sort can save a lot of carrying – I use an old milk churn.

Gradually the chicks cease to rely on mum. Now is the danger time for foxes, and all sorts of preventive gadgets are put out. But there is really nothing much you can do unless you are on the spot. Your predator situation should be under control by that time, so you must just feed like mad and pray and hope that the birds have taken to their home. Poor mum is now a bit tired of this game and has had precious little thanks from her foster children; so you can take her away, say 'Thank you' nicely, and hope she lays you a few eggs.

The brooder method involves an initial outlay, but if you can plan to use it for a number of years, the cost is remarkably low, particularly if you have everything made by 'a little man'. We had a house and ten partitions made for £25, but that was many years ago.*

You need a brooder house about five feet square and five feet high. This should have a flap at the front, which can be raised and act as a sun parlour as well as an exit. There must be a door or hatch to get in by, and fittings for the lamp for whatever kind of heating you use. Heating can be by electricity, bottled gas or paraffin. If you use electricity it is as well to have something in reserve, such as a calor gas heater in case of a power cut. The brooder should also have two more popholes for later use, if and when you use a side run.

---

*Messrs Gilbertson and Page Ltd. have an excellent catalogue which lists all the equipment required and much besides.

Next you need three six-foot high by ten-foot long partitions made of wire netting and battens. These should be made so that they can be bolted together when similar extensions are required. Hardboard should be nailed from ground level to about the three-foot level, as a draught excluder. Partitions and brooder should have carrying handles fixed so that the whole thing can be moved at one time. One of the three partitions which you require for the initial pen must have a door, since the fourth end is the brooder. You will need to extend the pen range to thirty feet, so you want another four partitions. If space permits, you can use the other popholes to provide exits to other pens. The roofing of the partitions can be made either of fruit-netting or light camouflage-netting which can be bought from a 'surplus' store.

In due course you will also need an acclimatization pen in the woods. This should enclose a piece of best quality habitat, providing sunny feeding areas, lots of low cover, and some good low roosting so that the young wing-clipped poults are able to learn to roost off the ground, safe from larger ground predators.

When planning your pen The Game Conservancy recommends that you should allow at least 20 square yards for each bird. Use less space and you risk severe disease problems subsequently even if not in year one. The fence itself should be at least six feet high, with the wire dug in or pegged out for a foot or so at the bottom, and a further foot hanging out as a floppy anti-fox fringe at the top. You can use ordinary chicken wire for the top two-thirds of the fence, but ¾" to 1" mesh is better at the base, just in case a stoat takes a fancy to pheasant for supper. Your pen will also need a re-entry funnel on each side, with one of The Game Conservancy's anti-fox grids recessed into the funnel, so that your charges can find their way to safety, but a fox cannot follow.

The brooder method requires day-old chicks which you buy from a game farm. These now cost about £80 per 100 depending on where you get them. You can send your own eggs to an incubator, but I think the small shoot needs all the wild eggs it has and I would far rather buy a few.

So having got your equipment all ready, and a few bricks lying handy to block up the odd gap where a predator might do something beastly, you turn the infra-red heater on to make the brooder nice and warm and await the Parcel Office's call. After the sorry tales I heard last year of day-old chicks, undelivered and dead in their boxes, it would now seem wiser to collect the chicks yourself and be safe rather than sorry. I always forget something; this time it is the floor of the brooder, which should be covered with shavings.

Well, here the chicks are. Take them carefully out of the boxes and put them within the surround, which you have already made. Composed of cardboard tied firm, this should be circular so that they can't crowd into a corner, and large enough to enable them to get away from the heat but not so large that they can get cold! It should be eighteen inches high in order to prevent them hopping over the top; otherwise there will be casualties.

The first thing to do is to tempt them to eat by placing starter-crumbs on white paper. Here there is no mum to show them the ropes, but a tap or two with your finger on the paper seems to do the trick, and they soon learn. A little beak-shoving into the jam-jar water helps them to find that too. Do not put your feeding and drinking utensils too close to the surround, nor indeed to the lamp – anything to avoid providing them with an excuse for crowding.

The correct height of the lamp must be found by observation. Start on the principle that there should be so hot an area directly underneath that they can't sit there and so must form a circle. So you raise or lower the lamp until you discover more or less the right place from their reaction. About fourteen inches to start with won't be much out. As they grow older, and so taller and less vulnerable to cold, you have to raise the lamp.

You must be 'on the ball' during the first 48 hours, but after this your troubles are mostly over. You can enlarge the surround and eventually remove it by the fourth day. About midday on their first day, weather permitting, they should be able to get out. Lift the flap or pophole and fix it, and coax them out with food and water placed outside; but always leave some of both inside, for those who need their artificial mum and don't feel like leaving her just yet. Shredded lettuce will keep the chicks amused and gives them something to come out for. Cabbage or kale is too coarse to start with.

Once out, the trouble is getting them back in again. I think the best method is to have a 'pusher', which fits right across the pen. Use the pusher as a stop so that they can't use the entire pen the first time out; a space of a few feet will do. Enter by the door and gently push the chicks under the flap or pophole and close it. It is fatal to think that they will go in of their own accord at an early age. They need the lamp and you must put them in.

Weather and age permitting, in due course they will all jug outside in groups, but do not let them spend the night outside until they are at least three weeks old. Once you know where they jug you may make a rain shelter in case of thunderstorms. But you must shut them into this area. Check the partitions and brooder to see that they are flush with the ground. It can do no harm to have a tunnel trap and the usual Warfarin-baited drainpipe, outside.

Once they are over the first stages, little supervision is required. They should be safe from predators, and provided you keep the food and water containers topped up they should flourish. Their chief wants are fresh ground and more and more space, which necessitates moving the pen and/or bolting on more partitions. The main danger is feather-pecking. It may be wise to have them electrically de-beaked or 'bitted' at the age of three weeks. Otherwise, toys such as kale hung from the roof, brushwood in the corner of the pen and shelter from sun and rain, all help to keep them amused.

At about six weeks they are ready to move to the acclimatization pen. It is quite a job catching them, and you must have some suitable containers such as game hampers in which to transport them. I choose a warm evening and release them carefully with just enough light for them to see where they are and be able to find a good place to jug together, which they are now used to doing. You will previously have fed and watered the pen, preferably using the utensils to which they are accustomed, and once again checked that it is predator-proof. Don't forget their chick grit. Lanterns, string-soaked in Renardine and any other vulpine deterrents can be used, and of course our old friends the tunnel trap and drainpipe are waiting outside the pen. A battery operated electric fence, about 9 inches to 1 foot off the ground is not a bad idea. Better still, two electric fences, staggered, one higher than the other at about 18 inches outside the wire. That ought to fox them!! Ha! Ha! says the Head Keeper wearing one of her many hats – that of Secretary! In the morning you hope they will wake up and start eating their heads off and thinking of this as home. Though they will still have their crumbs, at three weeks they can have a little kibbled wheat, and at five weeks some whole wheat or barley with their growers' pellets. Therefore they will now have to learn to scratch in the straw feed which also extends beyond the pen. Perhaps an old wild cock will come and teach them. And you hope they will soon learn to roost. If possible there should be some actual roosting trees or thick bushes in the release pen so that they learn to go up as soon as possible.

After 21 days, when they begin to find their way out, they should be used to the area and feel that the catering is so good that they don't want to leave. This staggers their departure, keeping a few in the pen as anchors, for a while after the first ones leave. Eventually, roll up all the side-netting so that the pen feed can be used *ad lib*. Wire netting left is dangerous and birds can be caught against it by the wicked.

The brooder method makes rearing comparatively simple, but there is one snag. Pen or no acclimatization pen, the ungrateful little so-and-so's do tend to stray – far more than the broody-reared birds. It is a good idea to park one or more broodies in their coops and, if necessary, with their chicks in or anyway near the release pens to act as an anchor. She can give warning if trouble threatens and she tends to exert a motherly influence on the poults even though they have nothing to do with her. However, if ground space or your pocket book permit, it is wise to organize one or more special stop feeds or crops in the most likely directions of escape. Say your pen is in a wood around which your ground extends well back on all sides except the east, where (as Figure 8 shows) you have only two small fields. If you can plan ahead to put one or part of one field into kale, so much the better. And, to back it up, place an extra feed on the obvious danger ways out of the wood – viz. the south-east and north-east corners. Then you will almost certainly have an existing feed on the main west–east ride. So your birds can work safely back and forth on the dangerous side, even without the attractions you may have arranged elsewhere, and if you feel brave when you shoot enough, stop the kale, blank the wood into the kale and have it back.

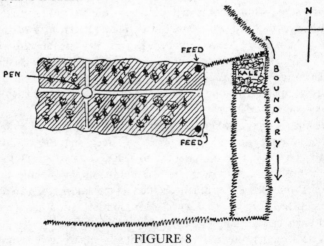

FIGURE 8

I prefer to work with wild birds. I am not too keen on reared ones, certainly in large numbers, but elsewhere wild bird stocks are not so good and some form of rearing may be a necessity. There is one method which sometimes works very well and is sometimes a complete failure. As it is such a gamble, many people are 'agin' it, but at least there is not much labour attached to it. You order (well in advance) hen and cock pheasants in the proportion of five to one from a reputable game farm. They now cost about £3.30 per head. It is interesting to note that the increase in price since 1962 is far less than anything else in pheasant rearing. The hens are laying-stock and the cocks picked breeding-stock; so at least you get good blood. You should stipulate first-year birds. These 'tired ladies' have laid their quota for the game farm by about the 27th of May, but have still got six to eight good eggs in them as well as the natural urge to make their own nest.

To await their arrival about the 1st of June (and every day counts), you make exactly the same sort of acclimatization pen as explained under brooder rearing, though not so large. This is the only work required and the pen must be big enough for the birds not to feel cramped. The experts say that if they fly from the hamper they must land in the pen. Release them at dusk, having fed and watered the pen. Remember that these birds have lived all their adult lives in a pen and have to get used to the wild state. Their success or failure to do this forms part of the gamble. Keep them as undisturbed as possible for not more than three days, then let them out and hope they will nest somewhere close or go into the corn – which should be up. A few eggs will have been laid in the pen; keep them and add them to any nest you find. Roll up the netting. I had one bird who brought off seven chicks in the pen itself. Keep on feeding it.

With advancing years, with much to do, and seemingly less time to do it in, I must admit that nowadays I only use the 'tired lady' system. Most small shoot keepers (part time and unpaid) will find that they simply have not got that valuable commodity, time, to rear birds any other way, unless they have a keeper or helper to share the burden. In addition, unless your shoot is on your doorstep you cannot protect a release or acclimatization pen properly, and you can well have a disaster from poachers or a bad fox if you leave it unvisited at night for any length of time.

The whole point of a small shoot, your shoot, is that it should be fun and a form of relaxation, a hobby if you like and I have found by bitter experience that looking after reared birds can be absolutely exhausting.

I now do not believe, again after some experience, that it is vital to have a release or acclimatization pen. You save a few precious egg-laying days, and anyway three days does not seem to be enough to acclimatize them, so we simply release them with some care from the baskets at dusk, having previously watered and fed the feed ride in the release vicinity. We try to let them walk out and off by holding a sack over three-quarters of the basket or box and easing them out behind the thickest bit of cover you can find. Try not to let them fly. They can, and should walk out. Don't let your helper chatter. It is a vain hope to think that next morning they will find your feed and start scratching around. You go through the motions, but the real reason behind releasing near a feed which has been regularly fed and used is that this feed is almost bound to be in a wild cock's territory. As already mentioned under the Ten Acre Shoot this gentleman will see off the wretched cock who comes with the hens and will add them to his existing harem, most of which should in the first week of June be busy with nursery matters. In this way the 'tired ladies' are less likely to stray as the territorial cock should give them other things to think about. Do not be too sorry for the pen cock, he has had a fairly long innings, with no competition!

The morning after the release on the Coats Ten Acres, there are some very odd pheasant noises indeed, and a blood row between the resident cocks as to who is going to 'look after' all these beautiful new ladies.

Unfortunately these girls do stray, or walk, in a most annoying and foolish manner and you simply must patrol the danger areas near where you have released them very early, the next day, and chase them back. Doing this may make the difference between success and failure with this somewhat idle and easy way of rearing. They will make a nest, all right, or at least most of them will, if the foxes don't get them, but it could be on your neighbour's if you don't do a bit of 'rounding up'.*

There are advantages in this method. The weather is likely to be mild, the cover will be well grown and may make up somewhat for any shortcomings in the bird's choice of a nest site. Also by the time the young hatch (you hope for four to six chicks), there will be plenty of corn to take them into and the silage will be mostly over. Therefore they should be flying when the harvest comes and shootable in late November; but be careful to tell your guns to leave them if you are doing an outside day in late October.

Whether you take the trouble to make a pen or release them on arrival is your affair, but where you do both is important. We release a hamper in various places all of which are wood or strip with cereal crops, for preference winter wheat, adjoining. The idea is that they should stay around in the wood as dark is coming on and perhaps move into the corn the next morning.

Thus, if the birds are going to stray, they have to go a fair way, and you hope that the urge to nest will make them settle down, territorial cocks notwithstanding. Do not worry about only getting four to six chicks. If every wild pheasant brought six to eight chicks to maturity, on an average, we should all be very happy.

I seem to have said a lot about the 'tired ladies' system of rearing. Nowadays we only get hen birds, having plenty of our own 'butch cocks'. You may not be so lucky, but I am sticking my neck out, possibly against Game Conservancy thought, in saying that maybe this system is nowadays virtually the only one possible for the small shoot.

November 1988 Here again experience has taught us that rounding up doesn't work. It often means that you simply haven't got time. They shouldn't go far and will not be allowed to do so by the 'butch' cocks. But get that fox problem under control.

Most people simply haven't got the time or the cash required for other methods. Quite apart from that, both here at Tower Hill and a somewhat larger shoot I have, this system has worked well over the years. There are really two provisos: that the Lord, in the shape of the weather, must be kind in mid-July when they hatch and that your predator, and particularly fox, control is really working when you release the birds in the first week in June. If it isn't, pairs of wings lying about are not exactly a sign of success! Perhaps most attractive, this method is also the nearest you can get to rearing a wild bird. Do you see what I mean? You release the hens first week June and then they are on their own and have to get on with it.

Both at Tower Hill on the 'Ten Acre Shoot' and my other small shoot, which is a syndicate, we have only used the 'tired lady' system for some years. The other shoot is farmed in what one could call a somewhat haphazard fashion, which has undoubted advantages. 'Fat Hen' is not unknown and we have some unsprayed rough bits, though we suffer from the farmer's cows settling in to what little cover we have. Yet, except for one year when we didn't get the dustbin foxes down properly, each year we have shot double what we have put down. This means that we put down 60 'tired ladies' and shot 120–130 birds, usually based on two proper shoots with a walkabout depending on the stock situation. But we never have a cock shoot. We want the survivors to look after the hen stock we leave and the 'tired ladies' when they arrive. On Game Conservancy return figures our results can't be too bad.

PARTRIDGE PROBLEMS

Looking back

IT is now over twenty five years since this book was first published. I mention, later on, some farming techniques which have altered, but it seems to me that two main things have changed in the shooting scene during this period. One is bad, the other good. Let us take the bad one first. It is simply that 'Big Business' people who are used to dealing with large sums of money, have applied these techniques to their sport and are thus rearing too many pheasants. They require large bags, perhaps because they are entertaining customers. In some cases where foreigners are paying large sums of money for the privilege of shooting in this country, they are not too particular how the birds are shown, the size of the bag being more important. Thus there is a lowering of standards, and it is hard to apply the word 'sport' to this sort of behaviour.

Perhaps this is plain speaking, but I know that there are many whose consciences are pricked by what one could call the 'numbers racket'. When I give pigeon lectures this subject often crops up at 'Question Time'. And these questions are asked by the real Grass Roots Sportsmen, the beaters and shoot helpers without whose aid driven bird shooting as we know it would simply fold. What can I say – you cannot defend the indefensible and I make no attempt to do so. The simple fact is that it is wrong on all counts to rear large numbers of birds merely to slaughter them.

The BFSS and The Game Conservancy are well aware of the

potential damage posed to all shooting by this group. Apart from any political overtones, it simply plays straight into the hands of the 'Anti's'.

Let no one think that I am against all rearing, I know very well how necessary it is to inject capital into shooting, so that fee-paying syndicate members get value for money and in turn there is something in the kitty to allow the shoot owner to pay the keeper and keep this side of estate management a viable proposition. We all like to get our guns off, but as in everything else in life there is a limit.

I very much doubt whether any of these so-called 'sportsmen' will read this book, as most of them have no idea about what goes on behind the scenes in a day's shooting, and they probably care less. They do not realize that perhaps four or five days shooting is the normal end-product of a year's hard work by a keeper. Nor can they understand the hopes, frustrations, anxieties and planning that go with this job.*

Why then do I put this piece at the beginning of a chapter on partridges? Because I think that if people want to spend a lot of money on their shoots, they would find it far more rewarding to rear more partridges and fewer pheasants. They would find that they have more actual shooting days, and more amusing ones and they would once again use some of the traditional partridge ground which on many estates has been left idle for too long.

When a lot of this southern area of country was part downland, as yet unreclaimed, it used to support a very large population of grey partridges but not many pheasants. Then along came the wars and the plough, and the pheasant population rapidly increased. The hen pheasant is a lazy creature and is inclined to park herself on a convenient partridge nest and lay a few eggs. Then she walks off, leaving the nest uncovered, and along comes the

---

November 1988 You can say that again. This mass rearing business is getting worse and worse, as I have already pointed out. OK, one understands that shooting is an expensive pastime, and a let day or two will help pay the keeper's wages. But can't we keep it within the bounds of decency?

first hungry crow. Anyway, the partridge understandably objects to this intrusion upon her privacy (she always covers her eggs when leaving the nest). Given this treatment, she deserts. What is more, unless it is very early in the season, she won't lay again; whereas a pheasant will almost always lay a second clutch if her first is destroyed. So, too many pheasants can mean fewer partridges, and, on large shoots where partridges take precedence, it is wise to keep the pheasant stock to a minimum, or to rely entirely on reared birds which will not affect the partridge's nesting programme. The small shoot, however, must be thankful for small mercies, and you must just hope that your pheasants will make their own nests. I do not recommend anyone except an expert keeper to tamper with nests, and this includes myself.

Old downland keepers will tell you that partridges and their broods used always to be found close to the nest, because there was abundant food. There was no need for the mad search for food which goes on today and which causes such losses. Such cereal crops as existed were usually less dense than on heavy land, and supported more weeds and so more insects. In wet weather there were always bare places for the chicks to shelter on. The light and porous soil quickly dried and there were any amount of natural dusting places. There were more sheep and sheep feeds (clover and rape) which kept them happy in the winter. There was no silage, and hay-making was done with a blade which a careful driver could always lift. Today there are a few places left, notably in Wiltshire and Berkshire, where areas of downland still remain unreclaimed. Where these are next to areas which are now in hand, the mixture can produce good bags of partridges far above the average obtained where only intensive farming is practised. To my mind this proves conclusively that the decline in partridges over the country as a whole is due principally to the lack of natural insect food for the chicks in the first three weeks of their lives. I admit, though, that to live on the chalk – that soil which grows everything from fish to pigeons – is an enormous advantage. And the same applies to all light soils such as the reclaimed alluvial in the fen country.

In 1961 I did some experiments in artificially feeding young wild partridges, which must have insects to survive the first two or three weeks of life. It is a horrid fact that even when a keeper has done his job, winter-fed, kept the predators at bay and protected the nest to the point of hatching, many of the young chicks will still die for lack of insect food; and there is nothing he can do about it.

This lack of food all comes back to that convenient whipping-boy – modern farming. Land is ploughed up early and seldom left fallow for long. Thus the period necessary for the incubation and hatching of insect life is not enough. Crops are sprayed and, with the best intentions in the world, the spray is blown into hedgerows and such headlands as are left or grass strips which are meant to be sacrosanct. Thus you may find that in a hedgerow 100 yards long there were three nests which all hatched out at more or less the same time, and well at that. Yet, in 48 hours' time, or even less, under similar weather conditions, you will find that one pair has still got fifteen chicks, while the other two are down to two or three, or maybe none at all. One can only suppose that the local food supply is simply not sufficient to sustain all three broods. What happens is that the pairs know that the chicks must and can eat only insects, and they take them off in a frantic search for food as soon as they are dry. Exhaustion and hunger, aggravated by the 'total' weather that June seems to bring so often nowadays, quickly causes the young to succumb. No parents could be more devoted or careful. It is simply that there is not enough 'scoff' to go round.

I have used the word 'total' weather because it seems that we either have torrents of rain and cold for days on end or an equally maddening period of baking hot weather, when the dew fails. I personally believe that dry weather can be as bad as wet. There must be moisture to hatch insects. Everybody expected that 1961 was going to be a bumper year. Ascot Week produced several cases of heat-stroke and this weather lasted a long time. But it wasn't a bumper year, and I think this was because it was too dry. I think, too, that the basic insect population is now so small that *any* extreme weather does them in!

So we thought we would be clever and solve the wild partridges' 'Junior Dinners' problem. We arranged to put out heaps of both pig and cow manure near nests that had already been located. And this before the hen had even gone down to sit. She can hardly fail to find this source of food when she comes off the nest, we reasoned, and, anyway, what about all these stories that the cock locates her food for her? After all, the heap is only ten yards away. Then when the young hatch, all they have to do is to bring them to the heap, ring the dinner bell, and there will be 100 brace first time over.

So the heaps were made, and protected with polythene sheets to keep the rain out and the moisture in. Both types of heap were seeded from time to time, with batches of 10,000 housefly eggs inserted into a mixture known as Peet Grady Medium. PGM provides the utopian nesting conditions for the fly which wants to hatch its eggs with all mod cons. The heaps were also topped up with fresh dung every ten days. Those made of cow dung were not a great success. They dried out too quickly and did not retain enough warmth to hatch out natural insects, though the flies in the PGM flourished. However, they attracted ant colonies, which was interesting as it was not thought that there were many ants left.

The pig dung heaps were a resounding success almost literally, and at the top of their form reminded me of the sort of dynamo noise I used to hear in equatorial Sudan. Everything came and laid its eggs in them and maggots flowed from every crevice. This, we said, is just the job, and we waited anxiously for mum partridge to be seen tucking in, when 'off', or Pa inspecting the heap as a suitable restaurant for his wife in her leisure moments. But no one saw either of them anywhere near the heaps, and when they hatched they never took their broods near them – or at least no one saw them. Moreover, I spent several hours with a pair of binoculars, being eaten by midges, which I suppose is some sort of retribution. But what hurts most was that every other mum bird in Hampshire had a lovely time, both before hatching and afterwards with her young. Pheasants, song birds, even moorhens all had a go, but no partridges. Well, there it is. Maybe the partridges did not like the polythene which shone a bit, though it was covered over. But no one else minded it. Maybe they got an indirect benefit through flies blown off the heaps by the wind; certainly there was a better than average showing of partridges on that bit of ground. But I can claim no credit for it. We just did not produce the right sort of bugs.

Elsewhere, we put down mealworms in shelters where the partridges were winter-fed. Pheasants and all other birds adored them. The partridges turned up their snooty little noses and said, 'No, thank you!' But baby partridges in captivity sucked them down from the age of a few hours, and there is no doubt that they are a most useful standby.

The only success we had was with the introduction of ant heaps which were put out on grass strips – away, we hoped, from the reach of nasty sprays. These definitely found a ready market, and if you know of any ant heaps, a little propagation is well worth while. I am no expert, but the most common ants we have in this country are *Lasius flavus* and *Lasius niger*. These yellow and brown ants hibernate underground in the winter and start operations in the spring. So you dig up the complete nest in April, hoping that you get the queen (it is little use trying to find her). Well worked nests have sparse grass on top. You put the nest upside down in a cardboard box, with the turf or sod end at the bottom, and transport it to its new site in a warm, dry, sunny hedge or grass strip. Here you dig a hole to fit, and tip the nest in so that it finishes the right way up. Then firm down the whole thing and hope for the best.

What happens is that the young queens fly off on a nice warm evening in July or later. They are then married in the air, their spouse falling dead to the ground. Afterwards they fly off and find a suitable nesting site on their own, often quite near the parent nest (we provided old tiles, slates, etc., for the purpose). The young queen then lays about thirty eggs. When these hatch she feeds the pupae, which in turn become the nucleus of a colony of workers. On reaching maturity these proceed to look after their old mum, who then turns into nothing but a big egg-laying machine. Thus the cycle goes on and thus, you hope, the number of nests increases, though it is a long-term policy. Both partridges and pheasants will scratch out ant hills for themselves and their young, so that this experiment is well worth trying. The trouble is to find the ant nests; old churchyards and unspoiled downland are good hunting grounds, though any keepers on the latter are apt to object somewhat. Don't worry about formic acid in ants or egg. Pheasant or partridge mums will see to it that the young aren't too greedy.

At last The Game Conservancy has come up with some answers to the partridge chicks' food problem. The conservation headlands technique, in which most of the sprays are left off from the outer 6 metres of the cereal fields, means that insects can flourish in an area right beside the nesting cover. The Game Conservancy report that pre-war levels of chick survival have resulted. All that is needed now is a return to good old-fashioned basic keepering and predator control, and wild game populations should increase.

Looking forward

At the start of this chapter I mentioned the 'bad trend', which I hope public opinion will condemn. Perhaps this is the place to talk a little about 'good happenings'. All that I wrote about the evils of modern farming still holds true, but at least certain things have changed for the better. Two of them stand out, direct drilling, and the emphasis on winter- as opposed to spring-sown cereals.

The mould plough turns everything over, destroying the cycle of insects breeding and rendering weed-seed food unobtainable. Direct drilling leaves a little cover, which can produce food and perhaps nesting shelter quicker and earlier than the normal drilling routine.

In those areas of the country where it is grown, winter

oil-seed rape provides food, and cover at a time of the year which the partridge could well call 'the Hungry Months'. In this area there is far less clover grown and the one-year ley seems to be out of fashion, so it is just as well that this relatively new crop has come on the farming scene. Harvested in July, provided care is taken by the combine driver, most broods should survive. Even my 'tired Lady Pheasants' might get away with it as the board is usually set fairly high.

Spring oil-seed rape took a beating in the 1976 drought and many farmers have gone out of it. Maybe the pigeon helped to reduce the yield a bit, but let me say here and now that this pigeon-shooter looked after his large acreage of rape with his usual dedication and refuses to take any of the blame! But French, or French cross partridges as well as pheasants are very partial to oil-seed rape – moorhens too. I well remember a small piece of new variety seed crop, where I was blamed for allowing the pigeons to eat it, and sat for hours awaiting non-existent pigeons, only to discover that the real culprits were moorhens!

Perhaps the most important change in farming techniques has been the change-over from spring to winter cereal planting. This gives the ground longer to remain undisturbed, though of course it will be sprayed. At least there is more winter food in the 'Hungry Months', and your partridges can be seen to appreciate the fact because it is on the winter wheat or barley that you will see them.

Collectively, these changes in farming practice must have helped the partridge, but let no one delude themselves into thinking that they now do not need to winter feed. This is still absolutely vital and will mean the difference between bringing your stock to the point-of-lay in tip-top condition or just alive.

So although it is true, as I have said, that the small shoot should rely mainly on pheasants, yet there is now much to be said for rearing a few partridges, particularly if the neighbours will agree on a joint programme. It then does not matter so much whether your birds stray to me or vice-versa. Thus everyone is happy and benefits. Also it is great fun doing a joint shoot, using both bits of ground, which means you can do some clever (maybe!) drives which you could not otherwise do, boundaries being what they are.

As regards actual partridge rearing methods, Game Conservancy Booklets Nos. 4 and 18 will tell you all about it far better than I can.

Perhaps the moment of truth for the small shoot starts when you want to move your partridges to a release pen. I am afraid that, as with pheasants, there have been some cases of people leaving their birds in a pen until the day they shoot, which is rather nasty and quite unforgiveable. But it is a fact that your release pen, or pens, should be sited in a field which has some existing cover, game mixture or kale, out of which the birds will be driven. If you put a pen in open ground your partridges are much more likely to depart, perhaps the greys more so than the red-legged. So the small shoot may not be able to afford the luxury of such a field. So what do you do – you put the pen in a driving strip or wood, a coppiced or open wood for preference. Perhaps the red-legs are a better bet for this game, as they quite like woods anyway and will come out with the pheasants. A friend of mine has had a dual pen, with both pheasants and partridges in it, they got on perfectly well, ate the same food provided, and stuck around when released in an almost embarrassing manner.

Under 'Feeding and Tactics' I have said that it is a sound idea to make your pheasant feeds before harvest for two reasons. To me these are important enough to warrant repetition. The first reason is that they have something to fall back on when their standing corn home is removed 'at a stroke', that popular expression. The second applies equally, if not more so, to partridges. Just as wild pheasants will play host to reared birds, so do wild (or second- or third-year reared ones if you like) partridges take over the young inhabitants of practically every release pen you provide. I don't think it is only for the water and food which you have thoughtfully placed both inside and outside the pen. I have seen adult partridges, often with coveys of their own, dance attendance on the young entry, very often on top of the pen, as if knowing they were soon to be released. Perhaps a so-called 'barren pair' or even one cock or hen French Partridge are more likely to take the young covey on. Incidentally, I dislike intensely this unkind word 'barren'. For how are we to know that this is actually the case, if some damned cat has frightened her off the nest and the word 'barren' can hardly apply, if her chicks have simply died of cold and starvation. But just as the local cock pheasant will take my 'tired Ladies' under his wing, if that is the polite expression, so do these partridges immediately become territorial birds and stick around with their new foster parents. I think this is rather important because it means that one of your main dangers with released partridges, that of an exodus, is averted. It also means that you can safely release them from the release pens three weeks before you shoot.

On a *really* small acreage your efforts must be directed mainly at pheasants, simply because you are unlikely to have a vast concentration of partridges unless there is something very special in the way of cover food. Early on in the year your best chance to get a few is in September, walking-up. When in coveys partridges are quite sociable, and you may see several lots quite close together on a field of mustard where the seeds have fallen. Your only chance to get at them is with a partridge drive, and the more limited your ground the more cunning you have to be to put the birds over the guns. Flankers, or flanking guns are more important than beaters. It is almost impossible to drive partridges where they don't want to go, and your local knowledge of their line of flight must be up to date. When you use flankers, much the best way is to let them start at either end of your gun line, taking in whatever bit of ground you require, until they reach their appointed positions. By all means have the horns of your beat in a crescent which will eventually join up with the flankers, but do not start the flankers with the beat.

Figure 9 shows a situation in which you fondly hope to drive your two boundary fields, which are grass and wheat-stubble respectively, into a field of mustard and then over the guns. If you know that the birds are happy to fly from the mustard to the barley-stubble where your guns are, and your normal westerly wind is blowing, they should fly across it. Partridges like flying across wind. The danger area is your boundary on the east side. You must decide whether to use one flanker starting on the left of your line of guns and two on the right (or east), or leave the left to chance and put all your flanking strength on the right where the chance of them breaking out is greatest. Alternatively, you can have five standing guns and use No. 6 as a flanking gun, who will be well away from the line. In any case make sure that No. 1 knows where the nearest right flanker ends up, which is just across the rather straggly continuation of the reasonably tall hedge behind which he is standing.

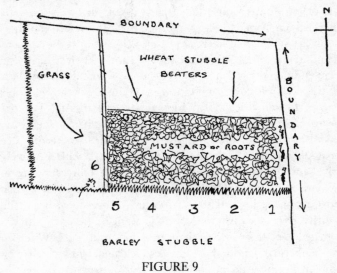

FIGURE 9

Let me stress once again two points which vitally concern partridges on a small shoot. First, wild partridges are the most territorial minded of all game birds. So do not worry about driving them off your ground – they will be back. Second, reared partridges do tend to stray, so a joint programme with your neighbours must help matters.

RUNNING THE SHOOT

NOBODY wants his small shoot to become a bore, and one of the main aims of this book is to prove that it can be a great source of amusement and interest without too much work.

You can hardly expect the average wife or young child to go round the traps, but it is a different thing with the feeding. This can provide quite an amusing walk for little Johnnie, and the feed bag is not too heavy (another good reason for putting out those storage bins!). Also little Johnnie can do what all small boys of any character like to do, and that is kick the straw around on the feed. Where feeds are hidden from view, he can stalk them, peer round the corner and report on what goes on. Two people can manage the feed bag and a tin of Warfarin. Apart from learning a little woodcraft when going round with you, it will do a boy (who will get a gun in a couple of years) no harm to learn the hard way that birds do not grow on bushes, and that there is more to it than just standing behind a hedge and letting your gun off. I personally think that a boy is better starting his shooting life with a 20 or maybe a 28 bore. A youngster can get quickly dispirited with a .410, with its small pattern. It is success, as in fishing, that makes an *aficionado*. Another reasonable bit of avuncular advice is one barrel only for two years, to concentrate the mind!

As time goes on, the 'admin' side of the shoot is becoming more important to me than the shooting itself, and certainly more important than the size of the bag. At its best, the small shoot must be very much a family affair and that means that it includes the wives and daughters of your friends, the guns. By all means have some beaters if the shoot warrants it, but do not be shy of asking your lady guests to help. Various cunning ways in which you can employ them and keep them warm at the same time are described later on.

Nowadays, shooting is becoming more and more of a social asset, and a far wider group of people now shoot than before. In this area, at any rate, it is rare for a farmer who owns his ground to let the shooting, and many tenant farmers take a lot of trouble to try to get the shooting rights into their own hands. Certain large estates owned by firms run their shooting as a form of entertainment or a commercial proposition. Whatever the reason, more people realize that a properly run shoot need not be quite so expensive as is popularly supposed, and that the expense incurred is of little account compared with the social and business connections made at the lunch-table or the covert-side. And, of course, it becomes a case of 'scratch my back and I'll scratch yours', so that the return invitations come in. All this is pleasant for the wife if she has any time at all for such matters, since she meets new people and can get away from the house for a bit. Entertaining for a shooting lunch is not difficult; nobody expects too much and everyone is in good form. But don't forget you are there to shoot, and sitting over the sloe gin when your beaters have finished their beer half an hour ago won't increase the bag, and, nowadays, may cause you man-management problems!

Apart from all this there is no doubt that many owners, particularly farmers, are becoming interested in the mechanics of shooting and are genuinely concerned to produce game as well as they would any other crop. And for this enormous advance, which must benefit the game stocks of the country as a whole, there is no doubt that the Eley Kynoch Game Research Station at Fordingbridge, as it was then called, was primarily responsible. Their mantle has now fallen on the Game Conservancy, so I take off my best shooting hat to both of them!

Obviously it will be the right thing to do to ask your neighbour to at least one of your shoots, and most certainly to tell him whenever you are shooting. Thus you may well find that he will say, with knowledge of your ground, 'Oh! Last time they flew over that boundary corner; put a gun there on my side if you like.' And you can do the same for him. Boundary hedges are often a source of friction. To avoid this, more particularly on the small shoot where they may be important, some definite arrangement should be arrived at between the two owners – as I have already suggested with regards to knocking off the rats. I personally don't think that boundary hedges should be fed unless by agreement. The Utopian, but probably impossible, way is to treat them as sanctuaries and never shoot them. But whatever arrangement you come to, you must know whether you can put a gun or a beater, or both, on the far side.

It is very difficult to drive partridges on ground of any size with less than ten beaters, let alone flankers. But, on a small bit of land, if you know the line of flight and don't mind the birds going off the ground, you and one other can probably put your only two coveys over your guns. Again, the average wood or kale field probably requires eight to ten beaters, though strips may need only three or four and hedgerows only two. But you may be doing a Coats manoeuvre involving one or two strips or converging hedgerows, and so you may still require eight to ten beaters in all, some of whom may have to be used as stops.

As a basis, then, for the shoot of any size, let us imagine that you require ten bodies in your beating line. Who are they to be? Now this is where some of the fun of running a small shoot comes in. On large and organized shoots, there will be (one hopes) a number of well-drilled beaters under the orders of one of more keepers; and likewise some stops, perhaps pin-pointed by the smoke of their fires. It is rather attractive to arrive at a shoot having driven through the beat for the day and seen various bodies patrolling their appointed beats and returning from time to time to warm themselves by their fires. This is all very well. But for your shoot, with its limited budget and the prospect of a meagre bag, it is simply not on. After all, your main hope is to get enough birds to give each guest a brace, and then see where you go from there. This may seem pretty pessimistic and perhaps is by no means the situation at your first time over, but it may well give you qualms on a cocks-only day, poor relations notwithstanding!

On the Ten Acre Shoot, which only takes two hours to do, I use the wives of my guest guns as beaters, and our one retainer, aged seventy, as a most unwilling stop; nowadays my friends the local keepers and farm manager always come to help and more elderly guests' wives, well wrapped up, become additional stops. I can assure you that no team could put up more birds, keep a better line and keep their sticks going more vigorously than these ladies, now aided by their children supervised by Under Keeper Lucy Coats. My daughter's language, when waving a flag at the Tower Hill birds to make them climb a bit, amazes me! I have no idea whatsoever where she learnt such words. Maybe we do shout 'Forward!' if a bird happens to get up, but this is an event, and it would be awful if the guns standing on my neighbour's ground were not to take the few chances offered them! Perhaps the ladies work so well because they know that at least they will get a good lunch afterwards to compensate for torn stockings, and maybe one old cock in the boot of the car if they are lucky. But, anyway, it is fun and that is what your small shoot should be.

I have acquired a reputation for ruthlessness when running a shoot. Wives or girl friends of guest guns, all camp followers are grist to my mill and after a quick 'sizing-up', I make use of them for odd jobs such as driving the Landrover, ferrying beaters, or acting as extra stops. It is also very useful to have someone to hold on to my hound, who is inclined to regard a day's shooting as a holiday from the pigeons. (Pigeon-shooting is lonely work, and I, too, enjoy a change.)

All this works very well, cuts down the cost and adds enormously to the day's pleasure.

People will tell you that boys are no good as beaters, and they may be right at that, but it is probably their own fault. I know that boys can become good beaters if you explain to them what it is all about and gradually train them. And, after all, you depend on beaters for the success of the day so that it is only fair to treat them as just as essential as the guns. While we are waiting to start, I always explain what we are going to do and why. I put the small boys in the easier places and those tough farm hands in the rough stuff, usually with a certain amount of back-chat. If you keep your beaters interested, it is half the battle. They like putting things up, and the more stuff there is the more enthusiastic they become. So if you tell them that a cock pheasant simply won't get out of a bramble bush unless they go in after him, they are much more likely to do so.

Now, about this shouting 'Forward!' and general noise during a beat. It may be correct in grand shoots for the only sound heard from the beating line to be steady tapping. But I don't believe, and never have believed, that silence makes the birds run forward any better; and as far as boy beaters are concerned, they like to proclaim their success at putting a bird up and I like to hear them doing it. Anyway, this particular 'keeper' is always exhorting, with suitable embellishments the 'right to come on', and then very shortly afterwards the 'right not to go so – fast', that it would hardly be fair not to allow them to make a little noise. Certainly at the end of the season I prefer to have them shout 'Cock forward!' lest my stock suffer.

You can soon weed out the keen and sensible boys from those who are simply after your money, and the survivors become regulars. In due course they can be trusted to 'go to the corner of the spinney and the five-acre and stay until the beaters join you – you have only two stands to wait'. Do not ask boys (or young ladies) to stop for hours on end. If I have to put someone out at crack of dawn, I have him relieved before the first stand, and he may even get a bit extra. It does no harm to cosset your beaters a bit. Hot soup on foul, wet days goes down well, and somewhere warm to drink it will be much appreciated. If everybody (guns and beaters alike) is going to have lunch in a barn, that is one thing; but if the guns are going to have lunch in a comfortable house, it is a bit much to expect beaters to sit out in the cold.

There may well be some old 'tack room' where a fire can be lit and they can get up a good 'fug'. If you can keep a stock of waterproof leggings or trousers and loan them out on wet days, especially when they have ten acres of kale to go through, they will thank you. But mind you get them back.

I like Landrovers because they contribute greatly towards the speed and efficiency of a day's shooting. Perhaps the worst thing a gun can endure is an interminable delay between drives. And for the aged and infirm long walks can be very exhausting. Some like doing things the hard way, but they waste a lot of time; though on a very small shoot the time question may not be so vital, except perhaps at lunch.

My motto is, try to avoid either beaters or guns waiting about. The intelligent use of Landrovers for guns, and a tractor and trailer for beaters, can easily result in an extra stand or two. If you use the latter to ferry beaters about (and, we hope, to carry all that game!) you may lose a precious beater, probably one of the farm workers, who will have to drive it. But you can often make use of him in other ways, such as flanking during a partridge drive (though always tell him what to do during the drive and in particular where to meet the beaters afterwards *and* which way his tractor should then be pointing). You had better make certain safety rules about the use by beaters of tractor and trailer. To start with, all straw bales used as seats should be tied down securely with rope. There should be no larking about or boys jumping off when it is in motion. It is a first-class idea to 'motor' round the perimeter of a partridge drive dropping people off, but they should be dropped off in groups to justify the tractor stopping. It does not matter if they talk on a trailer; game are so used to farm vehicles that I find it useful to explain the beat in the trailer, on our way round.

Beaters can wait quietly in their places before the start of a partridge drive, and after that the main thing is to keep their flags up and be on the look-out for any hand signals from whoever is directing the beat. I now use a horn, which experience has shown to be most useful, always providing that you explain at the start of the day what a given number of blasts mean and remember to use it as arranged. Again I really don't think it matters if they shout 'Forward!' when a covey gets up. When standing I am so deaf that I can't hear a whistle and am delighted to have some kind of prior warning. For a pheasant stand, I like beaters to make a lot of noise before they start so as to get birds running the right way. I am quite willing to be shot down about all this business of noise, though if the *guns* would make less cackle, particularly before a partridge stand, more stuff would come over their heads. Incidentally, this is one matter on which ladies, however charming, are apt to fall down.

The smaller the shoot, the more important it is to be on the best of terms with the farm workers. They must be the backbone of your beating line, because they know the ground and can be relied on to take charge of three or four beaters for some complicated manoeuvre; and of course one of them will drive the tractor and trailer, and will meet you as directed at the 'north end of the water-spinney' and not at the south – with the tractor wheel caressing one of the pegs at which your guns will shortly be standing! (You can bet that it will be old So-and-so's stand – a man who is famed for the efficient way in which he runs his shoots.) But it is in the out-of-season period that your farm worker can be most helpful, or otherwise. Care in driving tractors with cutters, willingness to point out a dangerously sited nest or to pick up eggs, all these things can add up to a lot of birds. 'I saw a stoat by the long belt at the water trough', can set you searching for an extra trap. And your feed and bales may need carting to storage bin or stack respectively. So I have put 'Xmas box to farm workers' on the Expenses List; it is a good investment.

While you should certainly treat your beaters right, there are some things that they must understand quite clearly. They must turn up if booked, or be waiting punctually to be picked up, even if it is pouring cats and dogs. It can always 'clear by eleven'. They must use not only their sticks but their heads, try to understand what you want them to do and, last but not least, they must realize that you want them to share the enjoyment of the day with you.

Finally, when the day is over it is a nice gesture to thank your beaters for their help, before or as you pay them. I wish that more of the other guns would do this if they get the chance. Obviously they have to see the keeper, if there is one, and get their birds. But after that, there is a tendency to nip smartly into their cars or into their host's house, in search of refreshment. On a small shoot, within the bounds of discipline, the more your beaters feel themselves one of the party, and are treated as such, the more fun you will all have. I fear that big commercial shoots are very bad for public relations between Guns and Beaters. They only see each other on either the lorry or Range Rover, never have a chance to talk to each other, and it is 'Them' and 'Us' and I hate it. It might be very salutory if one day a team of these vital 'cogs in the wheel' suddenly decided not to take part in a slaughter day (which they don't like anyway).

To return to the subject of joint or indeed any purely partridge-driving days. Unless it be a rather grand affair, which therefore does not come under the small shoot umbrella, such days provide an excellent opportunity for repaying people on the farm, or those who regularly help you on the shoot, with a little sport. However clever you think you are, some of the partridges, particularly on open ground will fool you. So you can have some standing guns, some flank guns and beater guns. All in all, far more people carrying a gun (and those hares!) than a normal day's pheasant shooting will stand. And in this day and age I think this is rather an attractive proposition, and it is appreciated. Obviously there are safety rules, and it requires a lot of organization. For instance, I wish I could say that everyone carrying a gun draws a number, and then numbers 1 to 7 stand, and 8 to 14 become flanking or beater guns. They then move up three after every drive. This appears simple in theory, but if there are elderly people in the party, who can't walk far, the whole idea falls flat on its face and you have to think again. In any case I am convinced that a 'bang' or two behind them makes partridges and indeed pheasants go forward rather better than anything else.

It is always a good idea to have a cock day, or some day during the season when your regular beaters or gun-toters take the stands, and the normal guns beat. The boot being on the other foot, perhaps these gentlemen will then learn to be not quite so rude about the guns' performance when faced with the hard reality and a critical gallery as well. After all, keepers on most shoots have their own cock day, when they invite their friends and helpers. And this is in addition to the organized hare-shoots.

I do not wish to end this chapter on a gloomy note, but it is absolutely essential that every possible kind of accident, from a beater falling off the trailer to gun-shot wounds should be amply and adequately covered by an insurance policy. Surely this should be a legal 'must', especially in today's climate of 'let' days, some of them with guns without much experience.

EXPENSES

HOW much should your small shoot cost? That obviously depends on many things, among others on the amount of trouble and work you put into it. But, generally speaking, the average shoot should be able to give you, your family, and a few friends a lot of fun, and set you back a lot less than most people think. A man who owns and shoots his ground starts off with a great advantage, and if he farms it as well then he can put a lot of the expense against that delightfully elastic product of modern country life – the Farm Account. On the keeperless shoot, the main expense items for the tenant are rent, feed and beaters. I suppose you should include your guests' entertainment, which assumes greater importance if it is not a very good shoot! I have dealt with rearing elsewhere, but let me say now that nobody should be put off by the thought of putting a few birds down, if space and time permit. With modern methods, the expense is greater than it was but the advantages from the 'good neighbour' point of view are obvious. Perhaps this is where the ex-laying-pen Ladies come in.

If you rent a shoot, how much you pay should depend a lot on past history, though if you get the lease for a period of several years you may be able to build up a poor shoot into a moderate one. It is surely much better, from both landlord's and tenant's points of view if a reasonable period is set for the lease, preferably with an option to renew. Nothing is more maddening than to build up a shoot, and then to have it taken away. True, there must be an escape clause, on both sides, for there are bad tenants as well as good ones. One hopes, however, that this book may give people some ideas on how to improve their shoots and, by increasing the stock and improving the habitat, raise the value of them. So don't blame me if the landlord ups your rent! The extra fun you will have had on those Sunday afternoons will surely make it worth it!

Leases on the 'Old Boy' basis are all very well, but they can lead to friction amongst the best of friends. So it is probably better to have the thing tied up on paper. For this purpose the B.A.S.C. provides an admirable shooting-lease document which can be used as a basis. Any special details which local conditions call for can be added.

Many aspects of modern farming methods are hardly conducive to the welfare of game, but at least there is one which is. The corn-drier provides the most marvellous food for both partridges and pheasants, if you are quick enough to get hold of the residue before the chicken fanciers. All small shoots should have a feed store which is both dry and rat- and mouse-proof. As soon as the harvest starts you must go and make up to the chap in charge of the nearest drier (corn-drying is thirsty work, which may give you a clue). His boss, we hope, is a friend of yours and possibly one of your guns. He may want something for the tailings, and if he does it won't be much. So don't worry, pay up – you will get it all back later on. I have explained how to mix it under 'Feeding and Tactics'.

On most farms there is usually a surfeit of straw, anyway, when baling is in progress. As I have said, you should try to use any broken bales and take them straight off the field for your initial feeds. But if there is any doubt about obtaining them, buy some bales (wheat or barle; bales should now cost about 50p and 75p respectively), and make your own private stack in a central place where you can get at them when you want them for the feeds. Four bales per feed should last you for the season.

Few shoots are so small that you never require the odd beater. Some people are quite happy 'walking-up', but except for those birds going back, few 'walked-up' birds fly so well as those that are driven, and later in the season, unless guns

walk towards each other and so act as beaters, the old cock
pheasants will not find their way into the bag. But beaters are
expensive creatures, and what was in 1962 25s and a bottle
of beer for those over eighteen, and 15s and some lemonade
for boys, very rapidly runs away with any proceeds from the sale
of game which you fondly hoped would go towards paying for
the rent. What can one do about it? The small syndicate, whose
members do all the work under a 'manager' (unlucky man!), may
well divide their numbers and take turns as to who stands and
who beats. But for those who have decided that they must have
some beaters, the first thing to do is to decide how many are
necessary and, for pheasants, how many additional 'stops' are
required. Beaters are now £10 to £12 a throw plus beer, and
£13, on a grouse moor, though that is money well earned.

A way of reducing shoot costs, which I think is fair
enough in this day and age, is for guest guns to ante-up
something, perhaps the cost of a beater, for their day's sport.
If there is a keeper, obviously he gets any largesse going, but,
as joint shoot organizer-cum-unpaid keeper, unless you have
much nicer friends than I have, you are unlikely to get much
of a hand-out at the end of the day! Let me explain this idea
in another rather basic way. Say, each guest gun gets a brace
of pheasants. In 1976 terms these are worth £3 in the unlikely
event that he wants to sell them. On your small shoot he has
probably not fired many cartridges and therefore, if there is no
keeper and he has not driven a long way, he could actually
make a profit! And you yourself can do with any surplus game
to sell towards shoot costs. In the same way, anyone carrying a
gun, who might on other days be beating gets his day's sport
and his brace of birds but is not paid as a beater as well. The
small shoot won't get much to pay the beaters without the sale
of game.

Obviously all expenses have gone up enormously, like
everything else, since 1962. Yet the small do-it-yourself shoot
can still get a lot of fun for far less expense than its 'brassier'
neighbours. Like the self-employed, the one thing you cannot

take into account is your time – so you must write it off as a labour of love. I certainly find the time spent not only on the Ten Acre Shoot, but on the other two that I run, very rewarding, not only to myself for a sense of achievement, but also for the obvious pleasure the results give to our guests and their families.

Some of us are getting on in years and are quite happy to have a morning's shooting, perhaps a long morning and then relax over lunch, knowing that you don't have to put those difficult boots on again. Perhaps the best example of such a day is our own Ten Acre Shoot which simply does not run to more than two hours' fairly concentrated action. But I have never heard anyone complain that my wife's gargantuan and epicurean lunch, plus suitable quantities of vino to help it down, has robbed them of their afternoon stands.

I have listed some of these various expenses, though the figures must vary considerably for every shoot and those given here are only approximate. You must do your own multiplication according to your acreage and needs.

You may be horrified by this formidable list of expenses unless you are an owner-farmer in which case most of them cease to exist, or at least you pretend they don't. But do remember to put your pleasure and those of your friends against the credit side. The only cash you can expect to see comes from the proceeds from the sale of game, or guest gun donation.

You had better walk the stubble in September for partridges if you have any. But it will pay you to have a walk round in October and kill a few cocks while you can get at them. At this time they fetch a fair price, but it is much better to take a little trouble and find a direct outlet rather than sell to a dealer. Generally speaking the public are prepared to sample and spend their money on more exotic foods than they were eleven years ago. Therefore you may well find an hotel or restaurant which will welcome pheasants or partridge on the menu. Anyone 'beefing' about current game prices must understand that home prices, including those for pigeons are dictated by the considerable Export Market demand.

Take it easy in October. The birds you expect to see in your coverts in November are probably out in the hedgerows, and if you clobber the lot your first time over will be disappointing. Mind you, we are not a grand shoot who have a cocks-only day first time over, and a very good idea too. Get rid of them when you can.

I am rather mean about hares. I like the party, particularly those extra walking guns, to shoot hares, as they provide good beater money. Leave large hare shoots in February to those who have plenty of ground. Most years hare prices fall with a bang during the organized February shoots, so the small shoot had better take advantage of the higher prices ruling during the shooting season. Most people like shooting rabbits and welcome their return. They are a financial asset, as well as providing a little more to shoot at on the small shoot, and they can now be kept perfectly well in control from the farming angle. If your cover is very thick a few good rabbit runs do help game to move about, and they also provide an alternative to your precious game for hungry vermin. In the old days beaters were always grateful for a hare or rabbit, but now they do not always want them. It is probably only fair to let the farm workers have the rabbits as a 'perk', if they want them. Otherwise you can repay those who help you on the shoot by giving them the chance. But, rabbits are coming back so it is only right from the farmer's point of view if you stipulate that whoever 'does' the rabbits makes a proper job of it.

How then can you decrease the inevitable cost of your shoot? The modern way is to have a syndicate. There are various types of syndicate, but whatever its basis, a syndicate means that your shoot is no longer yours to some degree, and you must weigh that up before you make a decision. A small shoot syndicate is best made up of friends. Nevertheless, if you are going to run it you must make certain terms. Firstly, it must be clear that you are the boss and will run the shoot from start to finish with the responsibility and authority which that entails. Secondly, the members must understand that, apart from their money, you will expect a few Sunday afternoons' work from them, improving what I believe are known as 'habitat conditions'; and also some help with the rearing, especially with such hard work as making pens or carting birds from rearing field to wood.

Certainly a good syndicate has many advantages. You may be able to solve your beater problem, with every member bringing one or two of them and being credited on the account. Then, all members know the ground and the drives and you have more time to control the beating line personally. On the other hand, you are tied to the same people every time and your other friends can't be asked since the small syndicate can't afford many guest guns. In larger syndicates, which may well be run by an estate office, guns will pay their whack usually before the season starts, and any overheads are borne by the estate or owner. But on the small shoot it is only fair to have a proper profit-and-loss statement made up, and any additional expenditure 'ante'd' up equally by the members. This is another condition I would make before taking on the job.

It is also fair that the enormous cost of petrol for a Landrover used for feeding or other shoot purposes (usually by the Amateur and Unpaid Keeper), should be entirely borne by the syndicate. Let me spell this one out. If you feel this idea is both just and fair, then you can alter the bit on the list of expenses I have shown accordingly. This means that if there are six members of a syndicate (including the Amateur Keeper) and the total petrol bill (let alone repairs!) is £50.00 then five of the members ante-up a tenner each. The Amateur Keeper can then feel that his time is not entirely unpaid.

I think it is a mistake to expect members to turn out regularly in order to do work out of season. There is always one who will shoot in any weather but finds a convenient excuse when any physical exertion is called for. But if it is small enough and all members are enthusiasts, this sort of shoot can be great fun.

EXPENSES

Expenditure

Rent (are rates included?) at £2–£5 for Forestry Commission and private land   ..   ..   ..

Cost of each feed based on 1 cwt wheat at £5–£6 per cwt and 1 cwt seconds barley at £5 (at least) per cwt

Straw bales based on wheat at 50p per bale or barley at 75p per bale ..   ..

Traps at £5 each   ..   ..

Petrol for use of Landrover during the season ......
gallons (up)   ..   ..

Beaters based on two main shoots, x men at £10–12 and y boys at £6–£8   ..   ..

Beer and lemonade for beaters ..   (up)   ..   ..

Special 'loan' clothing for beaters   (up)   ..   ..

Xmas box to farm worker or helpers (up)   ..   ..

Entertainment of guests   ..   (up)   ..   ..

Game given to guests ..   ..
(cost in at min. £3 per brace pheasants)

Total rearing costs, if any (keep a separate account for this) (all up) ..   ..

Extras (such as 'Keep-at-home' oil, seed, equipment for making hoppers or storage bins, tools such as hedgeknife and onion hoe) ..   ..

Umbrella Insurance (All Risks Policy)   ..   ..

———

Total Expenditure   ..   ..

Income

Game sold   ..   ..   =

Syndicate charges   ..   =

Guest gun donations   ..   =

———

Total income   Less Total Income

———

Total Cost

THE BIG DAY

By the beginning of November, sudden poaching disasters apart, you ought to know which wood feeds are the most popular and which leys or hedgerows are being used by your birds as recreation grounds. Now is the time to formulate a preliminary plan for your first 'big' shoot. It doesn't matter whether you are going to get fifteen pheasants or fifty; you have still got to work it all out. Your plan will be based on last year's experience and any recent October days, but far more important is the close observation of your birds' habits.

Quite apart from tactics, do not forget to lay on the beaters' refreshment and somewhere warm and dry for them to sit in. Also the cash to pay them with. No doubt your wife has got your guests' repast in hand. And, though it may be somewhat premature to think of this, you will want to give your guests young birds at the end of the day. Young grey partridges have yellow and the old birds grey legs, but towards the end of the season the difference is not so marked and the correct way of telling them apart, as used by dealers is as follows: the point of the outside flight feathers on each wing is sharp for young and blunt or rounded for old. With red legs or red leg cross there is usually a small white speck on the end of each outer flight feather. This denotes the young. There is no speck on the old birds and they have very knobbly embryo spurs. But, wearing my Game Dealer's Hat I can only tell you that even the most experienced keepers, yes, and the buyers for game firms, can both go wrong on this one. Needless to say Yours Truly gets the stick both ways. You can tell a young cock pheasant by his immature plumage and by his spurs which are not like the daggers of the old stagers. Hens are more difficult to distinguish, but young ones are usually smaller. You can do the most extraordinary things to a hen pheasant with a match, but I won't go into this. By far the best guide is Game Conservancy Booklet No. 9, *Sex and Age in Game Birds*.

Figure 10 shows a rather complicated stand which you must fit in to your first time over. Almost thinking aloud, I have tried to show the sort of rather muddled lines of thought which eventually produce a coherent plan and timetable. (Incidentally, I advise you to write your timetable out and give it a quick glance after every stand. I know this makes me less likely to forget to tell a stop or a walking gun something vital before he goes off with the beaters.)

In this particular case you have driven the six-acre from west to east for the last three years simply because it worked quite well and you were driving your birds home. Also the wind was usually right. But this year, as the sketch shows, there are some eight acres of kale one field away on the boundary. You could blank the six-acre into the kale (needless to say you are feeding it) and then bring it back. Would they go from the six-acre into the kale? You have seen half of them there already. Will they fly back well? Why not? There is plenty of room. You could try it. Stand your wife in the 'Long Field' where you think No. 3 should be, and walk the kale towards her with the dog. See what they do when they see her. But wait a minute; if you do it that way, won't you have one stand less? That is the only bit of kale on the shoot. You could make two stands of it – first the kale and then the six-acre. What about that one-year ley at the far end? Would that do for a stand in the afternoon? It's quite thick now and Tom says he saw several birds there the other day near the partridge feed. The cows won't be put in yet, surely, though you'd better check up. Yes, that might be the answer and you could make two stands of the six-acre and the kale for the next shoot, if there is any kale left. You must ask the farmer to 'strip' it from the boundary end, if it's all the same to him. Which stand will it be? It will take a bit of time blanking in the six-acre and the hedgerows; and you'll need at least two stops on the boundary side of the kale. They might as well bring in our side of the boundary hedge and then patrol about, but they must be there before the others start blanking in the six-acre.

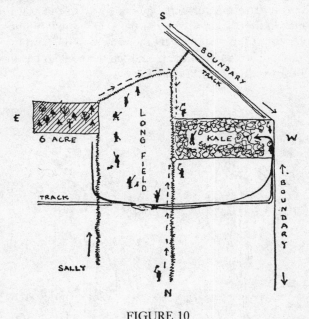

FIGURE 10

How many guns are coming? Will they all get in the Landrover, and who is to drive it? If your wife rashly said she would be ready to drive, can you hold her to it! Have you forgotten that the trailer is broken and you can't have it? That means the game, if there is any, will all have to go in the Landrover. That will be too much of a squash, so you must ask Bobby to bring his nice new one. Ah! there is your clue; Bobby is always late so you had better start with the kale and get the blanking in operation finished before the guns arrive.

If the beaters start at 9.10, you can finish the six-acre and the hedgerows and have the stops in position by 9.30. Without the trailer, it'll take the beaters five minutes to walk along the track and join up with the stops at the top of the kale. That makes it 9.35, so if Bobby (and his Landrover) aren't too late you can get the guns to the Long Field by 9.40. The pegs will be there, so you can place the guns and get your wife to run you round the track in the Landrover to join the beat – you'll be the only walking gun. Thus you must get the beaters to the farm by 8.50 a.m. so that you can brief them, and tell the guns to meet there at 9.30 sharp. (Better tell Bobby 9.15!)

This is the sort of jumble of possibilities that runs through my mind and ultimately helps me to come up with a plan. But I haven't stopped worrying yet .... . Now, what's my beater strength now? Ten less two kale stops leaves eight; that will have to do for blanking in the six-acre. After that, two more (one from each boundary) will have to go and bring in the Long Field hedgerow towards the kale and then stop at the junctions. It had better be young Charlie (his leg is not too good still), and old Frank who is a bit 'past' the kale. The rest, under Tom, can go round by the track and join up with the two stops, so that still leaves me with eight for the kale. Well, we'll just have to go slow and hunt the dog at the end – it's lucky it's drilled. Wait a minute, what about that hedge that comes into the six-acre from the south? There were three cocks there yesterday. Oh Lord! I simply can't spare a beater; what about young Sally? Her father said she could come and help. I must ring up and see if she can get over to the farm by 8.50. She can bring in that hedge while they are doing the six-acre and then go round with them and do a little kale bashing – at least it's not Marrow-stem, so she won't get lost. If it's wet she'd better go on the outside.

Now for the guns. I had better put No. 1's peg round the north-west corner in case they break there. Tell him to move up a bit towards the beat to start with. The others will be in the Long Field as far back from the hedge as possible. I must remember to tell them about the stops. Keep the right a bit forward. Tom can go there. Take the middle myself, and stand back.

Where did I put my waterproof trousers and the beaters? How long will it all take? Say I join the beaters at 9.45; about twenty minutes should see us 'out', so that means the beaters should be able to leave for the next stand at about 10.10. It will take them ten minutes' walk before they line out (wish we had that d—d trailer). There should be some partridges, so I must tell Tom they mustn't start before we are in place. I'll take Sally with me and we'll flank on the left. Then I can give them the signal to start. Tom can take the right again, so they should be okay, as they've all done this one before. Ten minutes for picking up and five in the Landrovers, so that we should be able to get to our places at the second stand about 10.20. So that's not too bad. I must remember to tell the guns (for once I've got two with reasonable dogs, so am economizing on a picker-up, which is probably a mistake) that they can go into the six-acre if there's anything down there as we won't be doing it again.

This sort of thing goes on in your mind for each stand, but once you have got the first one arranged in detail, the remainder are not so difficult. There is no need to work every inch of ground. Often I deliberately do not blank in certain hedgerows, so that some birds may escape and so provide more for another day. If space allows, leaving one stand untouched makes your second shoot more exciting. On your first day, when birds are relatively undisturbed, it may not be necessary to put out stops at all.

However generous the time allotted for lunch, I always find myself saying rather desperately, 'We really must go in five minutes.' This problem makes it worth while considering the continental method of shooting from 10.0 or 10.30 am to 3 pm without a break. You give your guns and beaters a quick sandwich and a glass of something about 12.30, and you probably ask the former to a late lunch. This method allows birds to get out and feed after being disturbed, and it provides continuity for your drives. But most beaters have their breakfast very early and require something more substantial than a sandwich at lunch-time. And I personally am so exhausted with 'First-time-over-itis' that I welcome a chance to sit down and collect my thoughts for the afternoon programme with the aid of a little refreshment. Perhaps the one thing I would alter after all these years is that any small shoot day, whether pheasant or partridge, may be better off without pegs. A change of wind or some other factor over which you have no control, can make a last-minute alteration in plan necessary. And if your VIP guest has not yet had a shot, you can always put him where you fondly think a bird might go. Big bag or small, the great thing to remember is that, before everything else, the small shoot is there to give maximum enjoyment to everyone.

INDEX